Annie W. Goodrich—

HER JOURNEY TO YALE

THE MACMILLAN COMPANY
NEW YORK · BOSTON · CHICAGO
DALLAS · ATLANTA · SAN FRANCISCO

MACMILLAN AND CO., LIMITED
LONDON · BOMBAY · CALCUTTA
MADRAS · MELBOURNE

THE MACMILLAN COMPANY
OF CANADA, LIMITED
TORONTO

ANNIE W. GOODRICH

~~~~~~

*Her Journey
to Yale*

by

ESTHER A. WERMINGHAUS, M.N.

The Macmillan Company
NEW YORK
1950

TO

Effie J. Taylor

&

Mary M. Roberts

ACKNOWLEDGMENTS

APPRECIATION is accorded for opportunities to consult original historical materials in the archives of the Division of Nursing Education at Teachers College, Columbia University, the Visiting Nurse Service of New York, and the Yale University School of Nursing.

For their time, thought, and hospitality, the writer is indebted to those who helped, through personal interviews, in the interpretation of events here presented: Naomi Deutsch, Edwin R. Embree, Lillian A. Hudson, Annie W. Goodrich, Laura M. Grant, Elizabeth Melby, Mary M. Roberts, Isabel M. Stewart, and Dr. and Mrs. C.-E. A. Winslow.

Without the friendship and assistance of Myrtie L. Carpenter, research secretary at the Yale University School of Nursing, this little book would not have been undertaken or completed.

Generous permission to quote from copyrighted publications has been given by the following individuals and publishers: the *American Journal of Nursing;* the American National Red Cross; *The Canadian Nurse;* Josephine Goldmark; Annie W. Goodrich; the Harvard University Press; J. B. Lippincott Company; Longmans, Green and Company;

Julian Messner, Inc.; *Modern Hospital;* the National League of Nursing Education; Amy F. Patmore; G. P. Putnam's Sons; and the *Yale Journal of Biology and Medicine.* Permission to quote from the Vassar Camp publication, *The Thermometer,* has been granted by Vassar College. All publications which were used in research are listed with the References at the end of the text.

The libraries of Teachers College, Columbia University, the Yale School of Medicine, Vassar College, and the Library of Congress have also given special assistance.

To the members of the editorial staff of the Medical–Public Health Department of The Macmillan Company the author would like to express gratitude for constructive criticism and a pleasant working relationship in which they have been at all times both patient and generous.

E. A. W.

Annie W. Goodrich—

HER JOURNEY TO YALE

HIGH in the heartlands of the Connecticut farm country northeast of Middletown, a white frame house of modest proportions looks out over a broad expanse of fertile fields. The sky is wide above the breathless sweep toward distant hills. From the elements of air and soil the sun draws life in fine, full measure. The wind blows over the countryside in majestic crescendos, or gently sings. Snow and rain come in their season like children returning home.

A remarkable lady greets the visitor at the doorway of the house. Her soft white hair crowns a figure which bends forward ever so slightly with the grace of a flower facing into a fresh breeze. Her delicately shaped yet capable hands are extended, and her grey eyes speak a merry welcome. Her eighty-four years are borne with a trace of vexation, although she is quick to acknowledge gratitude to the modern science of geriatrics for her presence on this planet. So vital and debonaire is her spirit that one feels an immediate sense of incredulity that time should wear so well. For all its thin etching of tiny wrinkles, her face has recaptured an expression recorded only in portraits of her as a young woman, before heavy responsibilities and fatigue had begun to mold her features.

Upstairs, a room under the eaves has been prepared with thoughtfulness for every detail that might add to a guest's comfort. Downstairs the table is laid and a cozy wood fire crackles cheerily on the hearth in the living room, where windows open out on three sides toward the far hills for which the house is named. The windows are framed, but not obscured, by gold-tinged drapes which accentuate the light streaming in from morning till night from three directions. Oriental prints and a carved teakwood table lend an accent of the exotic. It is a comfortable, bookish room, a room for pictures and letter writing and warm companionship. Whimsically, a blossom peeks in one of the windows from a vine outside.

Here at Far Hills for more than a decade the life of Annie W. Goodrich—Dean Emeritus of the Yale University School of Nursing—has been centered. Friends and relatives come from far and near to seek her counsel. She often ventures forth herself in pursuit of professional projects to which she has long devoted her being. Her feet which have walked characteristically in the beginnings of things still carry her forward. If you come to her for excursions into the past, you will have to probe and prod, and even then you will find yourself going away thinking, inevitably, of the future. With something of the same artistry she uses in tossing a salad or concocting a superlatively rich and decorative dessert called "Trifles" for a guest at Far Hills, Miss Goodrich will lead you to a contemplation of great issues. To her epicurean taste, flavor and spice are essential to a proper appreciation of all the serious challenges of life.

To look back into the vineyard of history through the eyes of a master and visionary who has labored there for more than eighty years was the privilege I sought when I went to visit her. What I most earnestly wanted to learn was the story of her professional journey to Yale. How was it that Annie W. Goodrich, in the fall of 1923, had become dean of one of the country's first schools of nursing to have an independent status among the schools and colleges of a university?

Surely New Haven must have seemed like the still, expectant center of a cyclone when Miss Goodrich, already renowned as an energetic and dauntless crusader, moved to Yale to become the first woman dean. Old Eli, hoary stronghold of masculine tradition, rocked the academic world in bestowing this honor on the representative of a predominantly feminine profession.

3

Yale's first lady dean might easily have been anathema, for she was known as a champion not only of nursing but also of women's rights. In the early days of the suffrage campaign she had been one of a small group of nurses who did not think it unseemly to take their places in street parades as members of the National Women's Party. After women achieved the vote, she continued to proclaim the increasingly significant role of women in social evolution.

Undergraduate Yale shuddered, both in private and in print, but her coming was a *fait accompli*. In February, 1924, the first class of student nurses took up their preclinical studies. Today, almost a thousand nurses number themselves among the alumnae of this school.

"There can be no surprise that Annie W. Goodrich is to be Dean of the new School of Nursing at Yale," editorialized the *American Journal of Nursing* for June, 1923. "Indeed, there is a certain inevitability about the appointment. Had she had this goal in mind, Miss Goodrich could hardly have prepared more soundly for the new task."

~~~~~

Mount Holyoke College had granted the honorary Doctor of Science degree to Annie Warburton Goodrich in 1921. Her reputation as an educator was vouchsafed by years as assistant professor on the faculty of Teachers College, Columbia University. She was the founder of the Army School of Nursing during the stormiest period of World War I, the staunch defender of quality nursing for the wounded at a time when pressure for large numbers of sub-standard nurses was at its height. Her deep democratic vision of community service was attested to by her constructive and noteworthy administration of the Visiting Nurse Service of the Henry Street Settlement in New York, an arduous function which she combined with that of teaching at Columbia in the years immediately preceding her appearance at Yale.

Her entire career, from the day of her admission to the New York Hospital Training School for Nurses, from which she was graduated in 1892, was that of a pioneer. Time and again she broke the ground and prepared the way for the many who were to come after her. Like engineering, medicine, and the law, nursing has grown from a craft for which apprenticeship was the sole preparation into a discipline of complex skills requiring sound intellectual background, broad experience, and balanced judgment for their best execution. The journey from apprenticeship to profession was one which Annie W. Goodrich had taken personally.

As a final step, the new school of nursing at Yale was intended as a demonstration which would consolidate the gains of a quarter of a century. It was to give living form to an ideal plan which had been forming itself in the minds of nurses whose visions were far ahead of the days in which most of them were, perforce, destined to struggle. Being given the opportunity to pilot this new school as dean was to be equipped with wings of old and great desire.

Dean Goodrich came not alone to the new venture. The story of the school, of the outstanding faculty contributions, of the cooperation given her within the university, the New Haven Hospital, and the city of New Haven, must be told some other time. It is the riddle of how a nurse became the first woman dean at Yale which posed itself to me. The solution was to be found, Miss Goodrich told me, in the story of the men and women who were with her in spirit, in inspiration now bearing fruit, and in dreams of the future when university schools of nursing would be accepted and supported by society as liberally as are other professional schools.

———

"Nothing is more untrue," she cautioned as we began talking about the road she had traveled, "than to assume that I have known only success, as people sometimes do. There have been proud victories—and also dark hours of defeat."

Since her own student days, Miss Goodrich has consistently taken a stand for all of nursing. No one school, no one field, can claim her unless it maintains an alert conception of its relation to the profession as a whole. Nurses speak of her as their "elder statesman." To her, the founding of a university school of nursing was simply one milestone, one battle won; her efforts for many years have been devoted to a campaign so comprehensive in its scope that the end is not yet in view. Her path, like that of nursing, has been a rocky, uphill climb.

Even today a confused public can still be heard

6

crying out, "What we want is nurses who can *nurse*, not maestros of paper work and theory!" Yet the tender and motherly ministrations of the nurse who is matured by experience and made wiser by a well-rounded social and scientific education cannot be said to be unwanted. An intelligent awareness of the therapeutic value of every task she may be called upon to perform—many of which would seem "menial" to the uninitiated—is the very essence of the nurse's craft.

Gradually, a new symbol is emerging to stand beside the compassionate but wistful "lady with the lamp." Miss Goodrich has referred to her as "the complete nurse." A few schools can produce a good many complete nurses, but it is Miss Goodrich's unfaltering contention that all nurses must be complete nurses before we can expect to realize the great social potentialities of professional nursing.

As Miss Goodrich talked, the subject became, not herself, but broad social trends and the impact which others have had on her thinking. It was to the pages of committee reports and professional journals, as well as to the writings of such men as Dickens, Tawney, Veblen, and John Dewey—the father of progressive education—that I was sent in search of many of the clues to her own story. Interviews with people who had been associated with her before she came to Yale helped me to gain perspective and to visualize some of the intangible details. The portrayal of her long fight for professional standards in Edna Yost's book, *American Women of Nursing*, was found to be of great help. Miss Goodrich herself

7

has given unstinting assistance through all the stages of writing.

~~~~~

Her journey as a nurse began one day in 1890. It was an age when "a child in New York City, lying abed on a winter night, could listen to the thud of hoofs on the snowy street outside and have a sense of a secure world," as one writer expressed it in *Years of the Modern*. The venturesome young woman who applied to Mr. George P. Ludlam, superintendent of the New York Hospital, for admission to the training school for nurses, had already seen through the illusions of a safe and almost perfect society which held the majority of her generation under their gossamer spell. Even so, she could not have been characterized as eager, for she went away from her interview without asking to be taken to see the wards of the hospital; she shrank from suffering and rebelled that it should be. She didn't want her determination to waver, but rather to carry her forthright into the hospital world with a job which needed to be done.

Students in those early days were selected on the basis of maturity, ability, and culture. Annie Goodrich was then twenty-four, and she had had enough contact with illness in her own family to make her feel that nursing demanded something more than the loyalty and devotion of an untrained woman. Education with tutors and in private schools, opportunities for travel, her father's reading aloud from the books of Charles Dickens during long winter

8

evenings, and above all her love and admiration for her grandfather, Dr. John S. Butler, remembered in medical circles as a pioneer in the care and treatment of mental illness in New England, were all in the background of the bold step she was taking.

"How clearly I recall the day I was to enter the hospital for my training," Miss Goodrich wrote in an issue of *The Henry Street Nurse* in later years, "spent, I must admit, more as if one were preparing for incarceration in a prison than admittance to a profession. A friend, distressed that her advice concerning the school had not been sought, insisted on at least a call upon Miss Maxwell, then at the old St. Luke's. How well I remember those dark and dingy halls permeated with the perfume of the pharmacy, through the shadows of which appeared a splendid, white-robed person. Her insistence that the school could not have been better chosen, and assurance of advice and assistance, calmed the trembling neophyte and reassured the anxious friend."

Miss Anna C. Maxwell, founder of the school of nursing at Presbyterian Hospital in New York and for thirty years its superintendent of nurses, was in time to prove mentor and friend to the fair-haired young woman who now appealed to her for last-minute advice.

In the early nineties nursing schools were still few and far between. Under the direction of superintendents of nurses who carried the responsibility of seeing that patients were cared for and students educated, the course was generally one of about two years on the hospital wards, with a few lectures in clinical subjects during off-duty hours. There was no preliminary course during which basic sciences and nursing arts were taught before the pupil began her actual ward duties. The head nurses were senior students, and much depended on their native ability to plan and teach the younger nurses as they went along. Irene Sutliffe, superintendent of nurses at the New York Hospital, relied firmly upon the judgment of the accepted students. "Great freedom— and great responsibility" were the pillars of her method of directing the nursing service.

The senior student who gave Miss Goodrich her initiation on Ward G at the New York Hospital was Lillian D. Wald, famous as the founder of the Henry Street Settlement. Though younger by one year, she always laughingly maintained that she was the "older," professionally, of the two.

Beryl Williams in her book, *Lillian Wald: Angel of Henry Street*, brings out that both were proud that their school accepted students of all faiths. Significantly, each held at the outset of her nursing career a unifying vision of service to humanity which cut with daring conviction through traditional barriers against understanding and cooperation. Annie Goodrich's admiration for the head nurse who could "recognize in a flash the thing that most needed to be done, and then somehow—with the willing help of others—see to it that it was accomplished" was on a par with her satisfaction in working with a nurse who managed the ward with the social grace which put patients, medical staff, and nurses at ease with each other, as people, from the beginning. The bond which these two discovered while working together on Ward G was to have a profound influence on American nursing.

――――

Very early, with twelve-hour duty the rule and assignments much too large to complete within this time, an inner conflict began to wage itself in Annie Goodrich's mind. When she left her own hospital, toward the end of her senior year, to go to the old Sloane Hospital in New York for her maternity experience, she met up for the first time with a more military system than she had yet known. And it was at Sloane that the strain on the honesty and integrity of the nurses, frequently deterred from exercising their own judgment, became almost intolerable to her.

One evening she failed to come to supper and her absence was noticed by Dr. Tucker, head of Sloane Hospital, who found her frantically bathing and weighing babies when he returned to the nursery. Asked why she hadn't eaten, she waved a hand in the direction of five more babies still to be bathed. His firm insistence finally prevailed, but as she left for the dining room, Annie's parting words were, "All right, I'll go! It probably isn't *good* for babies to be bathed by anyone who feels as I do, anyway!"

She was on the verge of tears, and she knew it. Underneath, her temper was raging at the dilemma in which she was placed. She wanted each of those little charges to have the care to which it was entitled, yet from early morning, day after day, more orders were given to each nurse than she could possibly carry out in twelve hours of rapid, ceaseless motion.

Annie went to her room that night firm in her conviction that one of two alternatives was open to her. Either she would have to give up nursing altogether—or she would have to begin a fight to remedy the situation with which conscientious nurses were faced. And so it was that, with her classmates goading her on, she drew up her "first list."

She sat down and outlined her day's assignment, with the time each item would have required if completed. When she added up the minutes, they came to a total of seventeen hours! In the morning she presented the list, with her protest, to Dr. Tucker.

The old Sloane Hospital was not revolutionized immediately following this incident. Nevertheless, Annie Goodrich had taken the first step along a path that was to lead to changes.

~~~~~~

The year after she received her diploma of nursing, she heard that difficulties were being faced by the training school for nurses at the New York Post-Graduate Hospital following the resignation of its founder, Dr. Julia C. McNutt. The Training School Society, organized in 1886 to assure financial support for the school, was on the point of giving up. A new position as superintendent of nurses was being created by the board of directors of the hospital, and for this position Miss Goodrich applied.

In May of 1893, she began her new duties, which

were to assume responsibility for the type of nursing service maintained by the hospital. She had no official connection with the training school but was rather to be a member of the faculty of the medical school and hospital. The president of the board of directors of the hospital was Dr. Daniel B. St. John Roosa, founder of systematized postgraduate medical education, in whom Miss Goodrich was to find a staunch ally.

"For the next seven years these two gallant souls labored unselfishly, faithfully, and earnestly side by side," writes Lena Dufton in the *History of Nursing at the New York Post-Graduate Medical School and Hospital*, published in 1944, who paints a happy picture of the "family spirit that made the hardest tasks mere play and obstacles mere trifles."

There were "bicycle trips up Second Avenue in off-duty hours, evening suppers where the *pièce de résistance* was the Welsh Rarebit, the acme of Miss Goodrich's culinary skill, and tea served in Dr. Roosa's office. . . . Both interne and nursing staff sat at one table in the dining room, with Miss Goodrich as gracious hostess. Her scintillating wit evoked much repartee and the mirth of those joyous hours is recalled vividly today by those who shared them."

The school of nursing at the Post-Graduate was unique in the extent to which it served the city of New York. Created out of the need to offer specialized instruction in the care of sick babies, this school also inaugurated the first trained nursing service at most of the hospitals of New York City. A fund to supply trained nurses in the homes of the deserving poor was instituted in 1887 by Mrs. Cornelius Du Bois, and students who had had at least six months of training were sent on these calls. Regarding the "Du Bois nurses" Dufton quotes a student of those days:

"Dr. Roosa continually reminded us that our hospital was built to serve the poor although it would offer accommodation to the rich. I used to report to Miss Lillian Wald in the first days of Henry Street and to Miss Whitelaw on the Upper East Side. Both were helpful in giving help and advice."

This must have been in Miss Goodrich's time, for it was in May, 1893, that Lillian Wald first received support for the work of two nurses on Henry Street.

The Post-Graduate nurses had affiliated with Presbyterian Hospital from 1887 until a school was started there by Miss Maxwell in 1892. Calls came from St. Elizabeth's, Nursery and Child's, the New York Infirmary, Manhattan Eye and Ear, St. Mark's, New York Cancer, and Roosevelt Hospitals. Babies Hospital was started as a ward on the first floor of the Post-Graduate Hospital nurses' home on East 36th Street. In 1894, according to Dufton, "the entire nursing staffs of the Roosevelt and Manhattan Eye and Ear Hospitals were composed of nurses from the school. The affiliation of the longest duration was that with Roosevelt, from 1891 to 1897, when it established its own school." Miss Goodrich's assistant, Mary Samuel, went to Roosevelt as superintendent of nurses in charge of this new school.

The new Post-Graduate Hospital on East 20th

14

Street, first occupied in 1894 after Miss Goodrich's arrival, was located within sixteen blocks' "walking distance" from the nurses' home on East 36th Street. The school could not afford to supply carfare. The curriculum as organized by Dr. McNutt, a nurse before she became a physician, was made up of lectures given during the evenings by professors of the medical school, who also included nurses in their lectures at the bedside of the patients. Dufton points out that thus developed "a camaraderie between the doctor and nurse that has persisted through the years."

Mrs. Ada Van Zandt, a laywoman of culture, efficient and willing to accept the responsibility, maintained the school through her own efforts from 1894 to 1897, serving as matron. Although having no official connection with the school, Miss Goodrich began to hold weekly quizzes at the home on 36th Street which came to be called "Class Nights." A student of those days, quoted by Dufton, writes that "Miss Goodrich . . . was a born teacher and taught her pupils not from classroom and lecture only but by personal demonstrations on the wards. She imbued her pupils with her own passionate interest in the intelligent and tender care of the sick and a never-failing loyalty to the medical profession and hospital. Her discipline was a spontaneous one, never felt, but elicited by her sense of fair play and the respect she engendered in all who came in contact with her."

Miss Goodrich became both superintendent and

matron, when the training school for nurses was, in 1897, made an integral part of the hospital. Under her direction, the curriculum was revised.

"There was a concept of human relationships in those early days, a concept worthy of analysis," she says in a chapter which she contributed to Dufton's book. "Social distinctions, with a few exceptions, were lost in the great rush of service. No task was too humble for nurse or even interne to stoop to if a need arose. Never did those students fail to meet the heavy responsibilities imposed upon them by day and by night; each class the best, for no class could be better; pioneers blazing the trail for those who were to follow, guided by the light that never shone on them.

"Each year furthered the professional recognition of this young school, as each year strengthened and broadened the curriculum. The affiliation with Sloane Maternity Hospital in 1899 stands out as a notable achievement. But the crowning event of those first seven years was the gift . . . of the Fahnestock Residence for the nurses."

Mrs. Fahnestock's nurse in her last illness, Miss Goodrich says, was Miss Merritt, an alumna of the school. Mr. Fahnestock, after his wife's death, asked Miss Merritt what he could do for her. Instead of asking anything for herself, she told him about the need for a new home for the Post-Graduate nurses, which he generously gave.

The opening ceremonies of the Margaret Fahne-stock Building were held on April 19, 1900, and on April 30th the alumnae association and medical staff gave a farewell dinner for Miss Goodrich, who was leaving to take up a new post.

━━━━━

Looking back in later years upon her seven years at Post-Graduate, Miss Goodrich realized that concern for her students there had added coals to the fire lighted in her own student days. When, in addition to twelve-hour duty, the nurses walked the long distance from the hospital to their residence, they often came to their classes in the evening hours so exhausted that their heads would nod or their minds wander. Driven by necessity at first, she reached out to the weary and learned to transport them beyond the consciousness of tired bodies and aching feet into the rare invigorating atmosphere of pure thought.

"If you believe a thing deeply enough yourself," she says, "you can always get others to believe. And when people believe, they are able to think and to see."

The period of Miss Goodrich's experience as superintendent of nurses at the Post-Graduate must be remembered for the activities of the New York superintendents in helping to supply nurses for the Spanish-American War—Miss Maxwell at Presbyterian, Miss Sutliffe at the New York, Mrs. Lucy W. Quintard at St. Luke's, Agnes Brennan at Bellevue, Miss Goodrich at the Post-Graduate, Mary Samuel at Roosevelt, Katherine Sanborn at St. Vincent's, Mrs. M. F. Dean at Mt. Sinai, and Mary S. Gilmour at the New York City Training School on Black-

17

well's Island. It was Miss Maxwell who led the campaign to gain an entree for nurses in the Army camps; Miss Maxwell, Miss Sutliffe, and Mrs. Quintard, who for the first time organized staffs of trained nurses in Army field hospitals during the yellow fever epidemic in 1898. Jane Hodgson, Miss Goodrich's classmate and close friend, was one of the nurses who served with them. Such associations, though she could not know it then, may have prepared her for the stand she would take in World War I twenty years later.

Miss Goodrich has often spoken of the help given her in her early days at the Post-Graduate, when there was no college to which she could turn, no other way in which she could prepare herself for administrative work except by doing it and seeking advice as she went along. Miss Sutliffe and Miss Maxwell were, in an informal and generous way, her teachers. "No hour was ever too late; no interview too prolonged for these two advisers," Miss Goodrich wrote in a 1922 issue of *The Henry Street Nurse*. "The wisdom of the following day's decisions was but the counsel of the night before."

Both Miss Maxwell and Miss Sutliffe, to whom she acknowledges this debt, were among the eighteen superintendents of nurses who banded together in 1893 to form the American Society of Superintendents of Training Schools for Nurses, which later became the National League of Nursing Education, an organization with which Miss Goodrich early became identified.

A movement to extend the period of nurses' training to three years gathered great impetus through the reports of thirty-four superintendents on the three-year programs they had actually put into operation by 1900.

One of these reports, presented at the 7th Annual Convention of the society, was given by Miss Goodrich. She tells of the program at the New York Post-Graduate, where in a hospital of 183 beds the "superintendent and matron" had one assistant, three graduate head nurses, and one night supervising nurse to direct the service, which was otherwise manned by students. Here, "in all contemplated additions to the curriculum . . . it was our plan . . . to increase the number taking the course in District Nursing, as we already feel the benefit both to the hospital and to the nurse of this valuable experience." Of 59 pupil nurses, 24 were able to have the opportunity of a three months' course in district nursing.

The report of the following day's discussion states that "Miss Goodrich thought that nurses in training needed to have insight into the conditions of various kinds of life, and advocated district nursing work in connection with social settlements as broadening and developing the nurses' character." Small wonder that Lillian Wald should one day say, "The gallant Annie Goodrich . . . was with us from the beginning in spirit."

Miss Goodrich, as superintendent of nurses, "administered discipline where and whenever needed with that perfect fair play and skill which has marked her entire career," writes Amy F. Patmore, one of her pupils at the Post-Graduate, in an article in the *American Journal of Nursing* for July, 1934. For many years one might not have discerned that she had her doubts about the pattern of autocratic administrator so generally accepted at the time. She has, indeed, been termed a "democratic autocrat." Yet she always spoke of "our" plans and in her dealings with students and staff was careful to do what she could to strengthen those who worked under her. She has stood on her own two feet, whether dealing with physicians, board members, or other administrators. In time she was to find the key to democratic administration which she handed on to others in her course in the administration of schools of nursing at Teachers College. Since no syllabus of the course appears to be extant, a study of her administrative practice would prove of the greatest interest.

~~~~~

When Miss Goodrich left the Post-Graduate in 1900 to become superintendent of nurses at St. Luke's Hospital in New York, she was asked to reorganize the training school. Here she encountered what was to her a new system of assignment of nurses' duties—a method which she says did obtain in certain other institutions and which was one day to influence her thinking in regard to the program at Yale. Each nurse at St. Luke's was given full responsibility for the complete care of a group of patients rather than for a group of specified duties to be performed routinely for all the patients on a ward. The latter method has always been quicker, but it tends to develop a mentality too much concerned with efficiency, too little with fundamental therapy.

"I learned a great deal at St. Luke's," Miss Goodrich remembers. Here she first started to think in terms of patient-centered methods of nursing care, later developed at Yale with the cooperation of the faculty and particularly of Miss Effie J. Taylor, whose previous outstanding work in psychiatric nursing at the Phipps Clinic in Baltimore signified her deep interest in the patient as a person. It was Miss Taylor who succeeded Miss Goodrich in 1934 as the second dean of the Yale school. In Elizabeth S. Bixler, an alumna of the class of 1927, this school has a third dean who cherishes the basic emphasis on patient-centered nursing care.

~~~~~~~

After two years at St. Luke's, Miss Goodrich returned to her own New York Hospital to serve as superintendent of nurses from 1902 to 1907. During this period she was elected to the chairmanship of the committee of the American Society of Superintendents of Training Schools for Nurses which was responsible for supplementing the financing of the course in hospital economics at Teachers College, Columbia University. Started in 1899, on the recommendation of Isabel Hampton Robb and M. Adelaide Nutting, the course was conducted until 1907 with the help of volunteer lecturers. When Miss Nutting came to Columbia in 1907 after years of educational achievement as superintendent of nurses at the Johns Hopkins Hospital in Baltimore, she took over many of the administrative details previously handled by the committee.

In 1910, following its endowment by Mrs. Helen Hartley Jenkins, the course in hospital economics was expanded and became the Department of Nursing and Health, with the committee under Miss Goodrich's chairmanship continuing to serve in an advisory capacity. In addition to the chairmanship of this committee from 1904 to 1913, when Miss Maxwell succeeded her, Miss Goodrich in the early years gave of her time as one of the lecturers for the course. Her association with Teachers College continued until she left for Yale in 1923.

"The greatest need of our schools will not have been met," Miss Goodrich stated to the society in 1905, "until in some way qualified instructors have been obtained, and qualified instruction demands a salary. . . . To confront institutions hardly able to meet their present debt with a proposition for salaried instruction seems futile, but the first and most important step towards the attainment of any object is an appreciation of its need."

~~~~~

One of her students at the New York Hospital was Mary Beard, who became a leader in the field of public health nursing. At the time of Miss Goodrich's eightieth birthday, Miss Beard told the alumnae of the Yale School of Nursing what it had been like in her day to study under their guest of honor:

22

"It was in 1902 when I first met Miss Goodrich. She came to the old New York Hospital to be Directress of the Training School, and I graduated the next spring. It was the era of the twelve hour day and the twelve hour night; classes after the day was over; a yearly vacation of two weeks; an hour a day off duty—if the time could be spared from the ward.

"We student nurses felt the stimulus of Miss Goodrich's personality from the moment she arrived. Classes were held during the daytime; more relief was provided to care for the patients, making it possible for the upper class nurses to learn more thoroughly the principles of ward administration. When the students were ill, Miss Goodrich took a personal interest in their care. When she left in 1907, deeply disappointed that the Governors could not see the light and had discontinued many of the reforms that had been started, there still remained a nucleus which could not be killed permanently. Miss Goodrich made it a School!"

Julia C. Stimson, who was to continue some of Miss Goodrich's most cherished work in later years, was another of her students at the New York Hospital. In an article in the *American Journal of Nursing* in July, 1934, Miss Stimson writes:

"The drawing out and the development of qualities in other people of which they themselves have no consciousness is indeed the proof of a great leader. Some people feel this influence upon them sporadically and with varying pressure. But it comes

23

perhaps to comparatively few to have a determined, far-sighted personality exercise a steady, quiet, but undeviating pressure consistently over a long period of years. This is what happened to me.

"My career as a nurse began under Miss Goodrich when she was superintendent of nurses in the New York Hospital. But here there was little contact between student nurse and superintendent. Things were different in those days and interviews with the Head did not have the effect of expanding my ego. On the contrary, I recall very diminishing results which probably were intended to be and were good for my soul.

"After graduation, however, and by this time Miss Goodrich had gone to Bellevue, the relationship changed. I had become a potential 'colleague,' though in my immaturity and inexperience I did not know it. It was at this point that I became aware of the 'influence.' Miss Goodrich sent for me and set before me three very different propositions. My choice of the position at Harlem brought me into a difficult and complicated situation where almost daily she counseled and drew out utterly unknown capacities; suggesting attitudes under stress, believing in powers to organize and create which naturally had to materialize, giving an example of inspiration to associates which had to be aimed at, encouraging at moments when it was most needed, and occasionally expressing warm appreciation of struggling efforts. Never could she have known what a brief note beginning, 'My dear child, I want you to know how well I realize, et cetera,' meant

The young nursing administrator, Post-Graduate Hospital, New York, 1893–1900.

Superintendent of nurses, Bellevue and Allied Training Schools, New York, 1907–1910.

after a particularly baffling and discouraging experience. Thus began the drawing-out or rather creation of qualities that just had to be developed because she expected them.

"At this period, organization, group effort, and meetings meant little in my life. I was busy, why bother about what other nurses were doing? One day, however, Miss Goodrich said, 'I am going to Minneapolis on such and such a train, on such and such a day, and I want you to come with me.'

"So small a thing to bother about for her, but what an expanded horizon for me, and what a course of action to have established in me! I have been going to meetings ever since. The development, the guidance, the kindly interest has been continuous since those days. But my good luck was not unique. There are hundreds of nurses who have had similar experiences and who, like me, will always 'rise up and call her blessed.' "

~~~~~~

With the reorganization of the Department of Hospitals in New York City in 1907, a new position —the general superintendency of Bellevue and Allied Training Schools for Nurses—was offered to Miss Goodrich. Here it was that Miss Stimson, at Harlem Hospital, first worked closely with her and began to feel the "influence." It was a relationship which was maintained in later years and acknowledged by Miss Stimson when she addressed Miss Goodrich in their correspondence as "Sister Anne."

The Bellevue position, Miss Goodrich remarked

at a dinner in honor of Miss Maxwell in 1922, was "big with creative opportunity, the greatest, I think it may truly be said, then offered in the nursing field, and carrying with it through a generous board all the advantages such a post should bring. It was Miss Maxwell who was urged and begged to take it. This she refused, pushing the younger woman in her place. And from the day she reached her decision to this, no one has heard her make mention of the fact."

While considering this position, Miss Goodrich took the examinations of the Civil Service Commission of New York State for the newly created position of state inspector of nurse training schools, which offered a much smaller salary but which she had pledged herself to accept if it were offered to her. Through the efforts of Sophia F. Palmer, then editor of the *American Journal of Nursing*, and other leading women in the New York State Nurses' Association, the post of inspector had been set up in the New York State Education Department for the first time. Miss Goodrich was asked to take the examinations and she had promised that she would.

Unknown to her, another nurse, for whom she had high regard, took the examinations at the same time. This was Anna L. Alline, associated with the course in hospital economics at Teachers College, who was to leave the college upon the arrival of Miss Nutting from Baltimore. Miss Alline, as it happened, came out first in the civil service examination.

The commissioner called Miss Goodrich to Albany and asked her to consider refusing the post, if, as a gesture to the group which had worked for the inspectorship, it were offered to her. An ardent Dickensian, it was a critical study of Dickens by G. K. Chesterton which Miss Goodrich remembers reading when she went out to sit for two hours under a tree in Albany, "thinking over" the commissioner's suggestion. Closing the book, she went back to inform him that she hadn't changed her mind. She had given her word that she would accept the position if it were offered to her. This she would have to do.

The inspectorship, in all fairness, went to Miss Alline. Miss Goodrich, happily, went to Bellevue, where both she and Dickens were very much at home. For here were the common people of a great city, to whose essential humanity Dickens had called the attention of the world, and who were to be transformed through visions which Miss Goodrich saw, over the horizon, of social evolution in which health is a signal of progress, illness a symptom of defeat and at the same time a challenge to community action. Bellevue has always been close to her heart.

The long hours of travel and waiting in the out-patient clinics which the patients of the city hospitals had to undergo in order to secure care caused her to spend much time in organization, trying to bring the facilities a little nearer to the people's homes. She thinks today of the crowded dispensaries with irritation and firm knowledge that, in spite of much progress in the meantime, a better way can be found to serve the halt and the lame who happen, often because of illness, to be poor.

~~~~~~

Miss Goodrich with a degree of regret gave up her work at Bellevue to go to Albany as inspector, on Miss Alline's resignation in 1910. It was felt that her seventeen years of administrative experience gave her the practical insight and authority needed in dealing with superintendents of nurses and of hospitals throughout the state. Her last evenings at Bellevue were spent learning to type, for she anticipated a need for an extensive and dignified correspondence. One of her first accomplishments in Albany was to secure the essential services of a secretary.

The uneven quality of nursing education was of the greatest concern to thoughtful leaders in the field. New York and Illinois were the only two states with definitely appointed inspectors. The registration of nurses was only eight years old, and not every state had as yet passed the necessary legislation. Edna Yost writes that in 1912 "It was estimated that ninety per cent of the nurses practicing nursing throughout the United States either had no preparation whatsoever or had been prepared through correspondence courses or in short-course 'schools' which meant a few months' experience in homes of the sick plus a little theoretical instruction. At that time no law in the State of New York, and in many other states, debarred anyone from calling herself a nurse and practicing as such."

Miss Goodrich's published reports of her years as inspector revealed facts which were to be used in the crusade for public regulatory control of nursing practice. Speaking before the American Society of Superintendents of Training Schools for Nurses in 1912, she said:

My study of the various laws, together with the knowledge I have gained during the past eighteen months, leads me to believe that in the New York State law we have more nearly approached the ideal than in any other. . . . The New York State law has, however, a great weakness—a weakness that retards our progress and handicaps the Education Department beyond words. Our law is permissive only, though in the face of the splendid and ever-increasing response on the part of the graduates of our registered schools—the number coming up for examination increasing every year—we cannot fear for the future; and the history of one state is but the history in a greater or lesser degree of every other. Nevertheless, I want to make an earnest plea for compulsory legislation—not who may practice as a registered nurse, or who shall practice as a graduate, trained, or registered nurse, but who shall practice as a *nurse*. I make such a plea for such registration, not for the protection of the nurse, but of the community. We are, in truth, public servants, and the knowledge that we should bring to our service is too great, and our responsibility too wide, for us longer to allow the individual institution for the sick to determine what our professional preparation shall be.

The legislation for which Miss Goodrich was working in New York State failed to pass during her term as inspector, a keen disappointment. Nevertheless, her influence was felt not only in Albany, but throughout the country. It became clear that a tremendous effort would have to be made to bring about a degree of nation-wide standardization of education and practice.

~~~~~~

The period around the time of Miss Goodrich's move to Albany—1910—is remembered as an epochal one in the entire health field. For nurses, it marked two educational advances: the establishment of the Department of Nursing and Health at Teachers College; and, under the leadership of Dr. Richard Olding Beard, the creation of the first basic nursing course in connection with an institution of higher learning at the University of Minnesota.

Physicians remember it as the year when Abraham Flexner's report on "Medical Education in the United States and Canada," financed by the Carnegie Foundation, first appeared in print—the year of the beginning of important reforms in the education of doctors, hitherto coming into practice from numerous small and inadequate schools as well as from the few larger ones of outstanding reputation.

A new concept entered the picture at about this time in the field of public health. The tuberculosis control movement, Dr. C.-E. A. Winslow writes, in dealing with "The Evolution of Public Health and its Objectives," had demonstrated the importance of attacking not only the problems of sanitation and communicable disease control, but also the personal habits of hygiene, through a vast educational program, if the health of the nation, and indeed of the world, were to be maintained. It was found that education in personal hygiene required the services of the physician and the nurse. Out of this development grew "the organization of medical and nursing service for the early diagnosis and treatment of disease" which has been steadily extending the scope of all the professions concerned with health since that time.

The need for standardization of education and practice in medicine, nursing, and public health—once visualized—started a chain of events still in the process of unfolding today.

It was this need which brought about the establishment, in 1912, of the National Organization for Public Health Nursing, on the recommendation of a joint committee of the American Society of Superintendents of Training Schools for Nurses and the American Nurses' Association, with Lillian D. Wald serving as honorary chairman.

Almost simultaneously, the Education Committee of the National League of Nursing Education started to work on a standard curriculum for schools of nursing which would serve as a working model for the average training school. The 1914 Convention of the League in St. Louis was presented with the rough draft of this "Preliminary and Partial Report on a Standard Curriculum for Schools of Nursing" which was finally completed in 1917. Miss Goodrich, a member of the Education Committee, of which Miss Nutting was chairman, presented the preliminary report.

The Flexner study of medical education was immediately suggestive to nurses. A year later the Education Committee of the League requested that the Carnegie Foundation make a similar study "on the whole question of the education of the nurse, inclusive of the fields of professional work which she occupies." This request was refused, but by 1912 the League was able to announce that the New York Academy of Medicine—as short a time ago as 1906 greatly exercised about "The Overtrained Nurse" —had appointed a committee on nursing education upon which two nurses, Miss Nutting and Miss Goodrich, were to serve. This committee had in view "forwarding a serious and critical study of the education of nurses, and the relation of the training school to the hospital."

Six years were to pass and World War I was to leave the heads of nurses "bloody but unbowed," however, before these efforts to forward a study of nursing education were to bear fruit.

~~~~~

The year 1914, which marked the outbreak of war in Europe, found Miss Goodrich—president of the International Council of Nurses from 1912 to 1915— in close touch with nursing problems abroad. This was the year that brought her back to Teachers College, her appointment as assistant professor making it possible for her to devote full time to teaching. Her special field was the administration of schools of nursing, her course in this subject becoming one of the most popular at "T.C."

Miss Goodrich looks back on her life at the college as a kind of idyll in which the nearness of great minds, stimulating books and their authors, and scores of promising students conspired to bring her the rich rewards which are to be found nowhere else but in the academic atmosphere. The scale of living was simple, but meaning was concentrated and rich in creative potentials. It is part of the wonder of Annie W. Goodrich that but a brief three years passed before another challenge came her way.

Her pace at the college was anything but leisurely. A full schedule of teaching, service as president of the American Nurses' Association from 1915–18, and chairmanship of the Nursing Committee of the Mayor's Council on National Defense in New York City, led to even greater contributions during the war period. She included each of her students, by careful plan, in her social life, entertaining many small informal groups at her home. She knew her students as individuals and spent hours in conferences with them. Late at night, she managed to read voluminously. She traveled and kept numerous speaking engagements.

The growing field of public health nursing was knocking more and more insistently at the door of Teachers College in the quest for special courses of preparation. By 1916, both the National League of Nursing Education and the National Organization for Public Health Nursing were working on recommendations for this new educational development in the profession, destined as we now know to open up an entirely new branch of nursing.

33

Miss Goodrich—long fascinated by the educational implications of district nursing—saw immediately the value of being able to draw upon this experience to broaden the horizons of the future nursing school administrators who were her students. When Lillian D. Wald approached her in 1916 with an invitation to take over the direction of the Visiting Nurse Service of the Henry Street Settlement, in conjunction with her work at the college, she made haste to place the suggestion before Miss Nutting for consideration.

~~~~~

M. Adelaide Nutting, director of the Department of Nursing and Health at Teachers College and one of the cofounders of the course in hospital economics out of which the department had grown, was not only Miss Goodrich's superior officer and close associate; it was Miss Nutting who first had drawn her into what came to be known as "the movement"— the studies, the thought, the vision, and the agitation for the university education of nurses. Miss Nutting's analytical mind had gone to the bottom of the problem of substandard educational facilities and practices, and had made her one of the first American nurses to champion the cause of the independent endowment of schools of nursing, precedent for which was set down by Florence Nightingale. Miss Nutting's book, *A Sound Economic Basis for Schools of Nursing*, is a collection of scholarly writings which takes its title from the initial essay and links her name most appropriately with an aspect

34

of the cause with which she will always be identified. Miss Nutting was the first nurse to hold a chair on the faculty of an American university.

These three—M. Adelaide Nutting, Lillian D. Wald, and Annie W. Goodrich—have come to be known as "The Great Trio" in American nursing history of the first quarter of the twentieth century. With them in the early years was Lavinia L. Dock, associated with Miss Nutting and Miss Wald in much of their writing. All four were suffragists, and all were possessed of broad social vision. Miss Dock was more extreme in her views than any of the others, more prolific as a writer, less often seen in the limelight, and not at all interested in power. Though she stood less and less beside the other three, she was always an influence in the background. She was the first secretary of the International Council of Nurses and for many years she wrote and edited "The Foreign Department" in the *American Journal of Nursing*. This relationship is interesting, in that the organization of nursing in this country grew out of the same impetus that brought about the formation of the International Council of Nurses at the World's Fair in Chicago in 1893. American nurses have maintained a vital contact ever since with their sisters across the seas. Through Dean Goodrich and Dean Taylor, the Yale School of Nursing was to find itself in the main stream of an international orientation.

The story of the long and uphill struggle to raise American nursing to the level of a profession, to extend the service of nurses so as to become a positive force working for the health of the community as a whole, is largely one which "The Great Trio" have written with their own toil. As Miss Goodrich explains, "Adelaide Nutting saw clearly the need for educators, administrators, and specialists for a rapidly developing social activity of profound importance. Lillian Wald, through an ever broadening social outlook, struck at the roots of society."

Miss Wald, whose function carried her beyond nursing even into the international social scene, sought in 1916 a director for the nursing service she had developed and the importance of which she realized, who could relieve her of the directorship while she continued to administer the activities of the Henry Street Settlement as a whole.

"If I accepted the appointment," Miss Goodrich related, "Miss Nutting at first felt I should relinquish my work at the College, since my subject matter was the administration of schools of nursing, not public health. To this I replied that in that case I would not accept the call, for my purpose in considering the directorship was in order to incorporate the demands of this field in my own, for the administrators who were to lay the sound foundations for nursing practice wherever it extended or developed. Miss Nutting then agreed to my joint function.

"A rich and rewarding experience followed," Miss Goodrich continued. "I have to say I believe I disappointed Lillian Wald because of my failure to desire a relationship to the Settlement. I saw settlements as a passing episode in social evolution; one of the last phases of philanthropy, its greatest contribution the opening of the eyes of the citizens of a democracy to their social responsibilities."

Miss Wald, on the other hand, was less of a social theorist. She saw the pressing, immediate needs and initiated action to relieve them. If private gifts were required, she set out to enlist the support of individuals; and if social support was necessary, she went to the mayor, to Albany, or to Washington with her colorful presentations of what the government's function should be. The establishment of the Federal Children's Bureau was just one of the outcomes of her own keen sense of responsibility.

When Ella Phillips Crandall, executive secretary of the National Organization for Public Health Nursing, heard of Miss Wald's appointment of Miss Goodrich as director of the nursing service at Henry Street, her comment was, "If she's going to continue to work at Teachers College and be director of the Visiting Nurse service you'll kill her!"

To which Miss Wald replied, "Well, then, she will go to a glorious death!" The work of nursing was always, to her, its own reward.

~~~~~

The interactions of the trio—Miss Nutting, Miss Wald, and Miss Goodrich—brought about developments which were to have significant influence on Yale's adventure in the education of nurses. The personalities of the three were in themselves partly responsible. Miss Goodrich, interestingly enough, characterizes Miss Nutting as standing for "The University"; herself as representing "The Common

37

Man"; and Miss Wald as embodying "The Case for Action."

People who knew and worked with the three in little old New York remark on their temperamental differences. Miss Wald was at her best in informal gatherings, where her presence was a warm and reassuring influence which somehow made everyone else shine as an individual—a little surer of the worth of his ideas and aspirations than he would otherwise have been. Miss Goodrich had an uncanny emotional power of setting fire to the imagination, of carrying a group, whether large or small, with her. "She could make you march faster than anyone," one of her former students at Teachers College has said. Miss Nutting appealed in the main to people who were predominantly thinkers and who were inspired by the breadth and scope of her mental processes. Between Miss Goodrich and Miss Wald there was always a current of sympathy which varied only in its intensity in different situations—between Miss Goodrich and Miss Nutting often a clash of opinion or a spark of antagonism, although they were loyal friends and shared many fundamental convictions. History records that to the willingness of each of the three to take new steps and to depart from established patterns or traditions much of the progress of nursing in the United States is indebted.

M. Adelaide Nutting was the scholar, the planter of seeds requiring years for their germination, the opener of doors, the historian of the past and architect of the future. When one thought of her, one thought of all that her profession owed to her as the instigator of new departures in the education of nurses. One thought of wise counsel given with the gentle expectation that reason and logic would prevail. It might not always be realized that she was a fighter, for her manner was an admixture of quiet charm and at times almost cool reserve. Nevertheless, her firm will and her brilliantly logical presentations of the case for the highest professional standards were successful in winning the day when there was pressure on all sides to compromise. Her chairmanship of the Education Committee of the National League of Nursing Education extended, except for two years, from 1903 until 1921, when Isabel M. Stewart succeeded her, and is a remarkable record of initiative in the step-by-step improvement of the curricula of American nursing schools. Nursing education in the United States will always rest upon the work of this committee as the firmest of foundations.

Behind the scenes, Miss Nutting was consulted when strategic nursing positions were to be filled. She held her protégées with a loyalty that was never one-sided. To be able to say, "Miss Nutting approves," was synonymous with saying one had received official blessing. Professor William Lyon Phelps of Yale University recognized Miss Nutting, in bestowing upon her the honorary Master of Science degree in 1922, as "One of the most useful women in the world!"

While one always associated Miss Nutting with the university—with Morningside Heights and Teachers College—one thought immediately of the Lower East Side and the Henry Street Settlement as the world of Lillian D. Wald, who was seldom to be seen anywhere near a classroom. Miss Wald was thoroughly in sympathy with what was going on upon the Heights, but her own school was the arena of life. Actually, there were many settlement houses administered by Henry Street, one as far uptown as 79th Street. One associated Miss Wald's name with the whole neighborhood settlement idea, as well as with the idea of visiting nurses. It was she who first suggested the term "public health nurse" and rural nursing to the Red Cross.

When one thought of Miss Wald, one thought of the spirit that transforms not only the drab and sordid outward aspects of daily living into expressions of poignant beauty but also the heart and the soul of the person who creates something for others to love. Around her at Henry Street she gathered people from all walks of life, from every race and creed, from nations far and near; in her presence all became neighbors whose hearts were joined in a common cause—the building of a more humane and happy world.

One never left her empty-handed, for hers was the soul of generosity. If she had only two pieces of candy, you would be sure to have one of them. Perhaps it would be a flower she would give you—or a present you once had given her! If you understood Miss Wald, you would take this as the highest compliment, for it meant that your gift had brought her joy worthy of being passed on to another.

During the last months of her life, when she was confined to her bed because of illness, she asked her friend and associate, Naomi Deutsch, who had gone from Henry Street to become the organizer and director of the San Francisco Visiting Nurse Association, then professor of public health nursing at the University of California, and finally director of the nursing work of the Federal Children's Bureau, to carry with her a message.

"Tell the nurses," she said, "as you travel about the country, that the *little* things are important!"

The contributions of Lillian Wald went far out beyond the field of nursing, but she also extended its boundaries. Her inclusion of service in homes and schools and in industry was indispensable to the full stature of the profession.

It was Miss Wald who likened Annie W. Goodrich to a torch, "a spirit afire." Miss Goodrich is described in the *History of American Red Cross Nursing* as being "of slender build, quick in her movements, with alert gray eyes and a highly organized nervous temperament. Her brilliant mental powers were expressed in instantaneous reactions and a flashing, rapier-like wit which often held a satiric flavor. . . . Hers was a practical idealism, best seen in the working out of difficult problems. She had a penchant for administration which amounted almost to genius."

"Wherein lies the secret of Miss Goodrich's greatness?" asks the *American Journal of Nursing* for July, 1934, in an editorial honoring the "Crusader" at the time of her retirement as dean of the school of nursing at Yale. "Not only by the standards of our own profession is she great. . . . Certainly it is true that, just as her grandfather pioneered in the field of psychiatry, so Miss Goodrich has pioneered in nursing. Challenged always by the new, she has given her whole self—with a zeal and devotion probably quite uncomprehended by lesser folk—to each new task." Hers was truly "a life being lived to the hilt." It is today.

~~~~~~

Reviewing Miss Goodrich's achievements before she came to Yale, I found myself at the offices of the Visiting Nurse Service of New York with the notes of the nursing committee during the years of her administration there before me, together with the issues of *The Henry Street Nurse*, in which she was constantly calling upon her staff to be articulate. Here, and in the moving quality of her own words, an impression of Miss Goodrich as the "Poet of Nursing" emerges. It is as though the administrative function were to her like living at the heart of a social organism, beautifully democratic in its relationships; and nursing itself the poetry to be created through the action of every nurse.

Here is her Forward to the first issue of *The Henry Street Nurse*, published for and by the staff, in December, 1920:

This little bulletin that makes its first bow over the threshold of the new year finds its inception in a keen desire that you, through whom our work is increasing so amazingly in extent, variety, and above all, in community value, should have the inspiration which is such an energizing force to us whose office is in the center of things and who through the pictures of your splendid daily achievement, have a vision growing clearer and clearer of the City Beautiful to be, our city, little, old New York.

A city block; no, one short street: 2,000 humans, 800 children in 40 buildings, and one, or better, two Henry Street nurses—connecting links between all that is sordid, wretched and that should not be, and all that is fine, constructive and that should and could be. Then, more and more streets, until finally a city, not to suffer and die in, but to dream and create in, and to look down upon from another planet in rapturous contemplation of the new machinery that we helped to evolve, with that soul-satisfying comment: "We told you so!" You do not know it, but this will be *your* creation, not alone, of course, for that would be a miser's paradise; but, through a generous contribution of thew and sinew, not to mention applied wit and wisdom.

The Henry Street Nurse is a colorful and many-typed individual. Will you not let her present herself as at least a black-and-white creation in words? It is time she was articulate, for she brings a message of the fulfillment of the dream down the ages of those high priests of progress, the poets. We, too, have poetry and art among us, as this little output proposes to reveal.

Miss Wald's greeting in the same first issue of *The Henry Street Nurse* is her testimony:

I rejoice that the Bulletin is conceived in the spirit of good fellowship and that each member of the staff will find inspiration in knowing what the other is doing—what her doubts and confusions are—what her encouragements are and what her vision is, as outlines of the vision become clearer with experience and knowledge.

It is more than a quarter of a century since the foundation stone of our structure was laid, and since

43

that time the Public Health Nurse has become an instrument of service throughout the world. It is proof of the vitality of our structure that it is not completed—that each day, as tower rises on tower, the view becomes clearer and we see more things to be done and the better way to do them. Here in New York we have unmatched opportunities to bring about the solidarity of interest among the nations of the earth, and the nurse has the door of opportunity opened to her because of the twin service of ministration and education that she can render. Modern standards of efficiency add dignity, in my judgment, to the essentially human kindliness of the nurse on her daily rounds, but efficiency and humanity are glorified by a conception of the far-reaching results that are pledged in the kind of service that we believe lies within our staff.

To the staff, then, I take this opportunity of declaring my comradeship and fellowship in their work and in the vision.

The first issue of *The Henry Street Nurse* contained a summary of a block survey conducted from November, 1919, to November, 1920; the Constitution and By-Laws of the Staff Council; a Contributors' Column; notes on new books called "Have You Read?"; a report from the Record Office showing statistics of the work; Staff Notes; and "A Student's Report." In the spirit of sharing, then, the publication sought to extend the effectiveness of each nurse's work, in an organization which had grown too large for one conference table.

When Miss Goodrich came to the Visiting Nurse Service as director in 1917, Miss Wald continued to head the Henry Street Settlement, of which the nursing service was but one branch. Miss Wald presided at the meetings of the nursing committee throughout the period of Miss Goodrich's administration, and rarely missed a meeting; in fact, her only absences were those necessitated by important appointments elsewhere.

The members of the nursing committee were lay and professional leaders whose interest centered in "the twin service of ministration and education" which Miss Wald believed in so deeply. Miss Nutting was a member of the committee from November, 1917, through the year 1923, when ill-health caused her absence; in January, 1924, Isabel M. Stewart of Teachers College was elected to the committee in her place. The names of other members would be a story in itself. One who must be mentioned here is Mrs. Paul W. Warburg, who was so intimately associated with the extension of district offices which took place while Miss Goodrich was there. With Miss Wald presiding, the meetings were given over in the main to Miss Goodrich's progress reports as director of the nursing service, the discussion of ways and means, and the formulation of policy.

~~~~~

Two actions of the nursing committee meeting on March 23, 1917, foreshadow many of the happenings of the next year—on the one hand the rapid expansion of public health nursing, and on the other the demands of impending and then actual war. Miss Goodrich was given authority to arrange with Miss Nutting for a student survey relative to setting up a visiting nurse service on Staten Island, under the

45

sponsorship of the Civic League. It was also agreed that students from Teachers College would give volunteer assistance to the Visiting Nurse Service as a "preparedness" measure.

War was declared on April 6, 1917. In May, Miss Goodrich presented the question of the organization of a staff council, a plan which the committee approved. In October, a recommendation was made to present to the board of directors the plan for opening to undergraduate students in nursing the rich opportunities for experience under the Visiting Nurse Service of the Henry Street Settlement, "together with the increase in cost involved in such an experiment." Giving preference to student nurses from New York hospitals, a training center was soon afterward opened in the Morningside district near Columbia University, with Lillian A. Hudson as educational director.

When Miss Goodrich submitted her report on the work of the nursing service for 1917, she announced at the conclusion that the work seemed so important to her that she had refused an urgent offer of national service abroad to continue to devote herself to the service of the district nursing work. Shortly, however, in February, 1918, the committee was to be informed of her "prospective absence in Washington during the period of the War to accept an appointment as Chief Nurse Inspector of the Military Hospitals with the Nursing Department of the U. S. Army." Reports of unsatisfactory conditions in the base hospitals of the Army had led to the call to Miss

Goodrich to make a survey; this in turn opened up such unprecedented possibilities that she could not refuse to go.

Her letter of resignation from the Visiting Nurse Service was tabled and she was granted a leave of absence. Later when she wrote to Miss Wald urging the settlement to accept her letter of resignation, as she did not want to be indirectly disadvantageous to the settlement by keeping her name on the Henry Street records, and stating that her "present colossal problem in the Army service" forced her absence to be of indefinite length, the matter was again kept in abeyance, in spite of the fact that Miss Goodrich at the same time sent news that the Army School of Nursing had been passed on by the Secretary of War and that she had been appointed dean. All the members of the committee agreed as to "the emptiness here without Miss Goodrich," and Miss Wald evidently continued to hope that she would return to them—as she did, in September, 1919.

~~~~~~

A full report of Miss Goodrich's activities in 1917 would find her associated with others in the vast challenge of preparedness for war. The pressures found in public health nursing were even greater in the hospitals of the country. As president of the American Nurses' Association, Miss Goodrich lived and toiled at the very center of all this stress. In June, 1917, an emergency committee made up of nurses, physicians, sanitarians, educators, and social workers was formed which, in August, 1917, became the Committee on Nursing of the Council of National Defense under the General Medical Board.

The burning issue in preparedness was the question of whether nursing aides should be developed rapidly as an emergency force to be sent abroad with the troops and help staff the heavily strained health services at home, or whether this might not be the time to expand the ranks of trained nursing personnel and put forth the utmost in efforts to improve the quality of nursing recruits and nursing education.

Bitter memories of the deaf ear Clara Barton had turned to nurses in the Spanish-American War in her zeal to enlist aides stood beside the demonstration of the superb services of trained nurses made by Miss Maxwell and others, which had resulted in the establishment of the Army Nurse Corps. Abroad, Britain and France were using the aide, and there was a loud cry for the United States to follow the European precedent.

Miss Goodrich and the Committee on Nursing of the Council of National Defense looked at this powerful ground swell with dread in their hearts. After searching discussions, they decided that it would be better in the long run not to succumb to popular demands which held nothing for the aftermath of war, when the healing forces of the world would be needed as never before in history.

Miss Nutting and Miss Goodrich were the courageous leaders who turned the tide favoring volunteer aides into a well of enthusiasm for the advancement of nursing education in this time of crisis. In a sense, the fight for the one tended to make them "see red" when the other was mentioned, but their prejudice—if prejudice it could be termed—rose from conditioning produced by experience.

Thus it was that one of the first acts of the emergency committee, according to material in the archives of the Division of Nursing Education at Teachers College, was to send out a letter of information to the presidents and deans of colleges for women and to coeducational colleges regarding plans for college women to enter nursing.

"A number of representative schools of nursing have, in response to our request, agreed to admit college graduates under especially advantageous conditions," stated the letter, which was signed by M. Adelaide Nutting, chairman; Lillian D. Wald, "head of our most important Visiting Nurse Association"; Julia Lathrop, chief of the Federal Children's Bureau; and Annie W. Goodrich, president of the American Nurses' Association. Writing to Miss Wald on June 1, 1917, Miss Nutting said, "Here is a rough draft of the letter to the Colleges, over which Miss Goodrich and I have labored. It now awaits your final touch. Miss Lathrop (telegram) is quite willing to add her name to this letter," which is to be "sent now in order to get the matter presented to graduating students before they disperse."

That the recruitment of college graduates for nursing was not a new thought is to be seen in the report of Julia C. Stimson, chairman of a "Committee on Approaching Women's Colleges," presented at the 1911 Convention of the National League of Nursing Education. Miss Nutting then reported that five colleges had asked to have nursing presented as a possible career to their students, and in 1912 Miss Goodrich told the League convening in Chicago: "Our place has been found in the institutions for the sick, but we shall never render our full service to the community until our place is also found in the university."

The Committee on Nursing of the Council of National Defense was composed of Lillian Clayton, president of the National League of Nursing Education; Mary Beard, president of the National Organization for Public Health Nursing; Annie W. Goodrich, president of the American Nurses' Association; Jane A. Delano, chairman of the National Committee on the Red Cross Nursing Service; Dr. Winford H. Smith, superintendent of the Johns Hopkins Hospital; Dr. S. S. Goldwater, superintendent of Mount Sinai Hospital, New York; Dr. Herman M. Biggs, Commissioner of Health in the State of New York; Dr. C.-E. A. Winslow, professor of public health, Yale University; Dr. William H. Welch, Johns Hopkins University; Ella P. Crandall, secretary of the National Organization for Public Health Nursing and also secretary of this committee; and M. Adelaide Nutting, chairman of the Department of Nursing and Health at Teachers College, Columbia University. Miss Goodrich, as president of the American Nurses' Association, was authorized to direct a complete census of nurses following the plan worked out in New York City by the Mayor's Committee on National Defense. Miss Wald was chairman of the subcommittee on home nursing and Miss Beard chairman of the subcommittee on public health nursing.

The names of those associated thus closely with nursing during the preparedness period are to be remembered when we come to the year 1919 and the Committee on Nursing of the Rockefeller Foundation which produced the long-desired report on "Nursing and Nursing Education in the United States," published in 1923.

~~~~~~

An important project of the Committee on Nursing of the Council of National Defense—also recorded in the archives at Teachers College—was the Vassar Training Camp. When Mrs. John Wood Blodgett, one of the trustees of Vassar College, approached Miss Nutting with a plan to train volunteer aides on the Vassar campus during the summer of 1918, Miss Nutting and Miss Lathrop, a Vassar graduate, succeeded in persuading her that here would be an unprecedented opportunity to recruit college graduates for nursing. Funds for the course came as a special gift for the purpose, placed at the disposal of the Red Cross. The donor, it may be noted, was Mrs. Morris Hadley's mother, Mr. Hadley being the son of President Hadley of Yale.

The preliminary three-months' course at Vassar was given in the summer of 1918 under the auspices of the Vassar trustees, with Professor Herbert E. Mills of the economics faculty of Vassar College serving as dean. Professor Mills some years before had resigned from the school board of Poughkeepsie as a protest against the appointment of an untrained woman in the position of school nurse, and had long been a friend of nursing. Recruitment for the Vassar camp was carried on by the Vassar alumnae. When it came to planning the course, however, advice was sought from the Committee on Nursing of the Council of National Defense.

The committee to work on the Vassar plan first met December 27, 1917, at the Cosmopolitan Club in New York, according to records in the archives at Teachers College. The notes of the committee state: "It was moved by Miss Goodrich and seconded by Miss Wald that the Vassar proposition be approved." The plan called for a preliminary course of 345 hours at Vassar and a subsequent two-year course of training in the hospital. None but college graduates were to be admitted. The details of the curriculum were worked out by a committee of the National League of Nursing Education of which Isabel M. Stewart of Teachers College was chairman. Serving with her were Elizabeth C. Burgess, inspector of the New York State nursing schools, and Anne Strong, professor of public health nursing at Simmons College, Boston.

Eliciting the cooperation of training schools to which the Vassar camp students might go when the summer was over was largely in the hands of the Committee on Nursing of the Council of National Defense, which drafted a letter to hospital trustees in February, 1918, pointing up "the urgent need for more skilled and capable nurses bringing a sound educational background. This is particularly true of the work in the modern field of public health, and in the several hundred hospital training schools for nurses, in which their assistance is specially needed in the educational developments which are so rapidly taking place. . . . It is felt that in the main these students will enter the public health field. . . . In view of the national emergency several representative hospital training schools have decided during the last few months to offer a condensed course of training of two years and three months for college graduates. . . . This has suggested to us the possibility of recruiting a larger group of college women . . . by offering them a very attractive intensive course of preliminary training."

The requirement of three full years of training in the hospital, instigated at the turn of the century, was by 1918 established by law in many states. With the movement to recruit college graduates for nursing, however, Miss Nutting and other leaders had come to believe that the real issue was not one of the length of a course of training, but rather of its educational content. It was now felt that the well-prepared student in a program planned according to educational principles could complete the course in a shorter period, approximately two years after the preliminary or preclinical course of three to six months. A time allowance for the college graduate had already been tried in several schools, Washington University in St. Louis being one of the first, during the period when Julia C. Stimson was superintendent of nurses developing the school of nursing there. The question was still regarded as controversial, and the Committee on Nursing in 1919, financed by the Rockefeller Foundation, was to make it a central focus of study.

The selection of training schools to which Vassar camp students could be assigned when the summer was over was thus limited in some states by the legal requirement of three full years of training in the hospital. Even where such laws did not exist, a few hospitals, among them St. Luke's in New York, the New York Hospital, Massachusetts General, and Peter Bent Brigham in Boston, were unwilling to cooperate, no doubt because of their confidence in the three-year standard. The Connecticut Training School at the New Haven Hospital was one of the thirty training schools in good standing which finally agreed to participate.

The Vassar camp had as instructors for the summer Dr. C.-E. A. Winslow of Yale; Dr. William H. Park and Dr. A. W. Williams of the Bureau of Laboratories, New York City Health Department; Helen Pope, professor of nutrition, Carnegie Institute, Pittsburgh; Dr. Florence Sabin, Johns Hopkins University; Louise Whitman Farnam, Yale Medical School; and the following nurses: Nina D. Gage, superintendent of nurses at the Hunan-Yale Hospital, Changsa, China; Anna D. Wolf, instructor at the Johns Hopkins Hospital; Maude Muse of the Lane Hospital School of Nursing, Leland Stanford University; Bertha Harmer, instructor at St. Luke's Hospital in New York; and Helen Johnson of the Presbyterian Hospital in New York.

〜〜〜〜

Among the outstanding names in nursing today are many who stem from the Vassar camp in 1918. Of the 550 applicants who passed every test, 430 students gathered at Vassar that summer, graduates of 115 different colleges, from 41 states and Canada.

Miss Goodrich was the speaker at the first convocation, held in the Vassar College Chapel on June 24, 1918, and the camp publication, *The Thermometer*, carries a report of her address:

"Miss Annie W. Goodrich, Dean of the Army Nurse's Corps [Army School of Nursing], after announcing in rather abrupt fashion that she had no eloquence at her command and little to say, thrilled her audience to successive bursts of applause as she pointed out the opportunities and the obligations facing them, kindling their imaginations at the same time by the suggestion that two years from now this group of carefully selected, skilled young women might properly assemble again to aid in the solution of new problems that might have arisen. She, too, called attention with impressiveness to the social problems which awaited solution, and that could be solved only by skilled women in the nurses' profession; making her point by reading, without comment, a brief list of juvenile offenders, ranging in age from twelve to fifteen years, who have been sentenced for their crimes to terms varying from 20 years to life, and this in a single state of the American Union.

" 'I have pledged myself,' said Miss Goodrich, 'to read this list to nurses in training at every opportunity, so that they may not forget one of the great obligations which rests upon their shoulders, to change the conditions of ill-health and bad-living which makes such a court record possible.' "

The criticism might here be made that Miss Goodrich seemed ready to place very great responsibilities indeed upon the shoulders of her profession. Yet we hear it said today that too much ground has been yielded in allowing artificial boundaries to be drawn up between nursing and the allied professions. Be this as it may, the nurse's need for social consciousness has always been crystal-clear to Miss Goodrich and is to be found shining in the background of a less flamboyant record—the carefully worked out curriculum for each school with which she has been associated.

The Vassar camp nurses who listened to her plea on the occasion of their first convocation were to be on hand for a greater emergency than they knew, for in the fall of 1918 the severe and devastating influenza epidemic struck at civilian and military installations alike. In a few months, the signing of the armistice caused many to feel, on the other hand, that the services for which they had volunteered were no longer needed. The January, 1919, *Thermometer* printed an inspiring letter from Dr. Winslow urging them to carry on, "to endure without acquiescing in what is inadequate." Many of these nurses did endure, for they had grasped the long-term vision.

∿∿∿

The plan for procuring nursing aides was so well under way when Miss Goodrich became chief inspecting nurse in the office of the Surgeon General

"The Great Trio."
Portraits taken between
1918 and 1923.
UPPER RIGHT
Annie W. Goodrich.
CENTER
Lillian D. Wald.
LEFT
M. Adelaide Nutting.

Dean, Yale University School of Nursing, New Haven,
at the time of her retirement in 1934.

in Washington in February, 1918, according to the *History of the Army School of Nursing* by Dorothea M. Hughes, that "one would have thought nothing could postpone it. Yet postponed it was. . . . Looking toward tomorrow and the days of reconstruction, she saw the possibilities of an Army School. She begged Col. Smith for time to collect data and present the plan in proper form. Col. Smith gave her the time she asked."

First came a tour of inspection of six military hospitals, in company with Elizabeth C. Burgess, on leave of absence from her position as inspector of schools of nursing in New York State. Innumerable conferences and committee meetings followed, with the final plan at last clearly outlined, and signed by Dora Thompson, superintendent of the Army Nurse Corps, Miss Delano of the Red Cross, and Miss Goodrich. While the plan was still under consideration by the War College, Miss Goodrich carried it before the 24th Annual Convention of the National League of Nursing Education, meeting in Cleveland May 7–11, 1918, where the American Nurses' Association and the National Organization for Public Health Nursing were also represented. What happened then is dramatically told in the *History of American Red Cross Nursing* published in 1922:

"Miss Delano, who was not opposed to the Army School of Nursing in principle but who firmly believed aides were needed to meet the total military requirements, was heard in her earnest plea to the assembly to be broad-minded. She was followed on the platform by Miss Goodrich, presenting her 'Plan for the Army School of Nursing.'

"Miss Goodrich spoke with her usual brilliant powers," the *History of American Red Cross Nursing* continues. "The chairman then called for discussion and a spirited rebuttal took place. Finally Miss Nutting threw her influence as a well-loved and trusted leader toward the acceptance of Miss Goodrich's plan.

"The nursing profession may well be said to have stood, on this May morning, at the cross-roads. Miss Goodrich beckoned at one fork for them to follow her, Miss Delano at the other. The tension of the meeting had grown very high. After further discussion, the chairman put the question to a vote. Miss Powell moved 'that the Army School of Nursing as planned by Miss Goodrich be endorsed by the three organizations,' the motion was amended to read 'as planned by the committee' and was passed."

The Army school was thus endorsed by the three organizations. Shortly afterward, Miss Goodrich says, through the efforts of Mrs. Frances Payne Bolton and Mrs. Alfred Brewster, lay friends of nursing education, a conference was arranged for her with Colonel Smith representing the Surgeon General, Colonel Hornsby, editor of *Modern Hospital*, and the Secretary of War, Newton Baker. Here Mr. Baker gave his approval of the Army school, with the stipulation that it should not interfere with enrollment in civilian schools. On May 25, 1918, the Army School of Nursing was officially sanctioned by the government.

Unfortunately, the discussions arising out of the Army school issue continued to mount after this decision was reached. On one side, according to Miss Delano as quoted in the *History of American Red Cross Nursing*, were Colonel Smith, Miss Goodrich, and their followers, on the other Dr. S. S. Goldwater and a large group in the American Hospital Association. Miss Goodrich remembers that Dr. Goldwater's support of the Army school at a crucial juncture probably saved its existence. Nevertheless, the shadows of the opposition aroused at this time were to fall across the path of professional nursing for many years.

The recruiting campaign for the Army school was carried on by the Red Cross, the Federation of Women's Clubs, and the state nurses' associations throughout the country. In five months, almost eleven thousand applications were received.

Participation of civilian hospitals in the training of student nurses for Army services in affiliation with the Army school was worked out by a committee composed of Miss Delano, Miss Goodrich, Lillian Clayton, Ella P. Crandall, Dr. S. S. Goldwater, and Colonel W. H. Smith. Approximately 200 civilian hospitals offered to affiliate with the Army school, among them the foremost training schools of the country. Through funds provided by the Red Cross, public health nursing instruction was made available to students of the Army school at the Henry Street Settlement and Teachers College in New York, and at the University of California. By the date of the armistice, 1,099 students were on duty in 25 hospitals, 567 more were awaiting assignment, and a total of 10,689 applications had been filed.

~~~~~~

The first class of the Army School of Nursing graduated in 1921 in two widely separated parts of the country, one group at Walter Reed Hospital in Washington, D.C., and the other at Letterman General Hospital, San Francisco. Standing on the steps of the Walter Reed Hospital to review the students who came marching past before their graduation in the afternoon, Miss Goodrich told herself she mustn't become emotional. She looked for a moment at General Ireland, who stood next to her, and was surprised to see that his eyes were filled with tears.

The Army made Miss Goodrich a second lieutenant for two weeks so she could go to San Francisco to take part in the graduation exercises at Letterman General. Here it was that she paid homage to the inspiration of the Army school in her address, "The Vanguard of an International Army":

There is a memory that should always be with us, the way in which a great country came together, men, women, and children, rich and poor, for a great project—the destruction of a threatening evil, the safeguarding of the things we held most dear. This is a memory to be cherished for itself and for those concerned, but above all must we retain it because it points to a fact of most profound importance to the builders of the future; namely, that given existing evils and knowledge concerning methods of destroying them an intelligent society should not permit them to continue, for it has again been demonstrated

60

that it is possible to unify minds scattered over a vast territory into a great effective force. . . . "As one lamp lights another nor grows less," so shall you light a million lamps upon a thousand hills whose penetrating rays shall guide and guard the stumbling, halting steps of our civilization on its long pilgrimage toward the ideal.

The students of the Army school must indeed have tasted the sweet flavor of a victory well earned. They had, like the Vassar camp nurses, served selflessly in the influenza epidemic of 1918. With the news of the armistice, and no assurance as to whether they would graduate, they had known an even deeper sense of restlessness and possible futility. It was March, 1919, before they received the first intimation of the permanence of the Army school. At this time, 548 of their number had declared their intention of carrying on to the day of graduation.

"Had Miss Goodrich done nothing else than build the Army School of Nursing," wrote Julia C. Stimson in the July, 1934, *American Journal of Nursing,* "she would have a forever shining place in the history of nursing education, but how much else she has done! Her 'Blue Birds,' however, to whom she gave the chance to serve that they longed for and that 'something more' which was to be of lasting value all their lives—a sound professional education —will never forget, nor will the younger sisters who have followed after."

Once the permanence of the Army school was assured and the program at last stabilized, Miss Goodrich—ardent pacifist, democrat, and practical administrator—joined in one more battle before returning to those who were waiting for her in New York.

On the question of rank for Army nurses, which was under intense and widespread discussion, it was her opinion that the nurse, to be effective in securing supplies and privileges necessary for her patients, required the authority which rank would ensure. In view of the constantly changing personnel in Army hospitals, she felt that the head nurse, especially, needed to waste no time in teaching the new men her real status. As often before in her career, she sought also for her successor the prerogatives which she herself had not enjoyed. She well understood that prestige is not to be put on and off like a chevron on the sleeve or a metal bar on the shoulder, but a quality rising out of the opinions others hold of the individual. The battle of rank was, to Miss Goodrich, a matter of organizing facilities for the welfare of the patients in Army hospitals. Therefore, when relative rank was granted to Army nurses she was glad that a step had been taken in the right direction. Her successor as dean of the Army school was *Major* Julia C. Stimson. When full rank was accorded to nurses in World War II, Miss Goodrich was profoundly grateful.

〰〰〰

For some years *The Modern Hospital* magazine carried a section entitled "Department of Nursing" conducted by Annie W. Goodrich and Carolyn E. Gray, first dean of the University School of Nursing at Western Reserve. Here is printed Miss Goodrich's paper on "The Nursing Program of the Army" which was read before the 20th Annual Convention of the American Hospital Association in Atlantic City, September 24–28, 1918. Here also Lillian Clayton, president of the National League of Nursing Education, writes regarding the variety of clinical experience planned for the Army school students: "We had all been thinking in terms of affiliation now for a number of years."

The term "affiliation," if confusing to non-nurses, is better understood when it is remembered that, even today, only in the largest medical centers is a sufficient variety of clinical experience available to give the student nurse certain essential contacts with the specialized branches of medicine and therapy. Thus to balance and round out her experience, the practice of cooperative planning has evolved through which experience in several or even many different hospitals and health agencies is arranged for the students of one school.

One of the historic affiliations worked out by the Army school was that in public health nursing, with the details of which Miss Goodrich had much to do on her return to Henry Street in 1919. The Red Cross early in 1918 had appropriated $25,000 toward the cost of training students at the Henry Street Settlement, provided Henry Street agreed to furnish four nurses a year for five years to the Red Cross Town and Country Service. Miss Wald in a letter of February 25, 1918, to Chairman Harry P. Davidson of the American Red Cross War Council, had written referring to Miss Nutting's emphasis on the obligation "to teach the nurse to be a teacher," and noting the cooperation of Teachers College in giving theory "while we give the intensive field for practice." She also made note of Professor Winslow's opinion that the public health nurse would make up the nucleus of one of the greatest of future professions, "whose entire aim and method of approach is characteristic of modern world tendency to shift the emphasis from legal and restrictive to educational measures."

The request of the Army school for a four-months' affiliation was granted by the nursing committee of the Henry Street Settlement on November 21, 1919. *The Henry Street Nurse* for April–May, 1922, carries a cartoon by M. Hana picturing Miss Goodrich and inscribed:

> With us—
>> At the beginning of our training
>> At the end of our training
>> Always!

Portraits of Miss Goodrich during this period show her looking out at the world with lustrous, tired eyes. She wrote to Miss Nutting of feeling as though a hurricane had passed, on her departure from Washington after the war. To her staff at Henry Street, and to her students at the college, where she resumed her course in the administration of schools of nursing, she brought a sense that here, in a great city, was the important work of nursing yet to be done.

The housing problem was one of the first to be dealt with on her return. Rooms for twenty students from the Army school had to be arranged for. Furthermore, since 1918 Mrs. Paul W. Warburg of the nursing committee had interested herself particularly in the various offices of the Visiting Nurse Service; one by one the cramped and dismal quarters were being exchanged for better ones. The need for substations became apparent, and when Naomi Deutsch, then supervisor at the Morissania office in the Bronx, hit upon the idea of using abandoned saloons, Mrs. Warburg and Miss Goodrich were enthusiastic. A period of rapid expansion of office space was started, with new centers being added, in addition to the substations. In all this work, Mrs. Warburg gave of her time and means, that the offices should be well furnished and attractively decorated.

Miss Goodrich recognized that her supervisors were carrying a great responsibility. Among themselves, she called them her "executives." Finally she proposed to the nursing committee that their title be changed to that of field director, in order to give full recognition to their administrative function. Today it is interesting to look back and see that the nurses of this group have become notable leaders in the profession—Dorothy Deming, Alta E. Dines, Naomi Deutsch, Emilie G. Robson, Irma Reeve, and Amelia Grant all were there, as well as Mary Brackett, who later became a pediatrician. Miss Goodrich's assistant, Rebecca Shatz, carried the administrative responsibility during her absence in Washington and celebrated her twenty-fifth year as a Henry Street nurse in 1920. She was a stabilizing influence drawing them all into a close and informal relationship and giving patient oversight to the multitudinous details of day-to-day management.

The philosophy of this group is outlined by Gertrude Hodgman, educational director, in an article entitled "The Demands Democracy Makes upon Supervision in Public Health Nursing" published in *The Henry Street Nurse* for June–July, 1921:

Democracy demands that work which is worthy to be done must be of the sort to allow the persons doing it an opportunity for individual freedom and growth. This, in turn, means the development of shared knowledge and interests within the work, and knowledge of its relation to other works and interests. . . . It is for the supervisor then, to help balance these two demands: the demands of the sick, and the demands of the nurse as an individual. In this problem, she must become the educator of the public, bringing them to see their responsibility for illness as well as the nurse's, and making them sharers of a common problem.

The development of statistics which created graphic pictures of the work to be used in education and study is attributed to Miss Montanye, who took charge of the record office in 1912, continuing in this capacity until her death early in 1921. Of Miss Montanye, Miss Goodrich wrote in the March, 1921, *Henry Street Nurse:* "Her death shook our structure to its foundations, but without a break, with scarcely a jar, this coordinating center, through the staff she had gathered around her, with the machinery she had evolved, carried on its work day by day

66

until her mantle fell upon the shoulders of a young, ardent, and gifted spirit that could again present in shapes and pictures the history of the street."

The need for more adequate cost accounting was a matter which Miss Goodrich brought to the attention of those carrying the financial responsibility for the Visiting Nurse Service. As a result, an analysis of the "cost per visit" to be prepared by Loeb, Traper Co. was authorized in October, 1921. In January, 1922, the National Organization for Public Health Nursing was asked by the Metropolitan Life Insurance Co., which was finding this problem of cost difficult to evaluate for all the public health nursing agencies with which it had contracts for nursing services for its clients, to create an impartial committee to make a study of "cost per visit" and report back to them in three months.

Miss Goodrich's report to the nursing committee for March, 1922, discusses at length the problems of overhead, cost of production, and suggested means of curtailment during the financial depression. At this time it was necessary to lengthen the working day to cut the cost per visit, and to dismiss ten members of the staff. By January, 1923, however, a special budget committee was able to recommend the addition of twenty-three new staff members and general salary increases.

Miss Goodrich gathered data regarding sick leave, vacation periods, etc., from other visiting nurse associations for comparison, and again asked the staff to take up an insurance plan. Social service had been added to the organization in 1919 with the help and advice of Florence M. Johnson of the Red Cross, familiar to war nurses returning from overseas through her untiring efforts to help them, whatever their need. Under the Social Service Department, special provision was made for the care of sick nurses, with Mary Magoun Brown in charge of the work. Funds for the care of sick nurses, who had served with the organization more than five years, were given by Mrs. Paul W. Warburg and members of her family.

The sum of Miss Goodrich's accomplishments at the Visiting Nurse Service of Henry Street Settlement can only be surmised. Mention of some of the things that happened as a result of group action, and always part of the vision of Miss Wald, while Miss Goodrich was there, is suggestive:

Formation of a staff council; institution of a staff publication, *The Henry Street Nurse;* development of a Social Service Department; affiliation for nurses of New York City and of the Army school; establishment of new centers for nursing service; institution of the custom of holding nursing committee meetings at the nursing centers, moved by Mrs. Warburg; growth of the numbers of students affiliating with the Visiting Nurse Service; distribution of *The Henry Street Nurse* to graduating classes of about a dozen of the important schools of nursing; introduction of the use of the Social Service Exchange; participation of the nursing service in the Public Health Institute held at Grand Central Palace in November, 1921; analysis of "cost per visit" by Loeb, Traper Co.; preparation of an eligibility list for use in nursing replacements, Miss Nutting's suggestion; opening of the office in Westchester, to be self-supporting; opening of new Board of Health prenatal clinics, after a meeting of Dr. Copeland of the Board of Health with Miss Goodrich, Miss Wald, and Mrs. Simkhovich of Greenwich House; centralization of the night delivery service in affiliation with Berwind Clinic; participation of Henry Street Settlement in the intensive experiment at the East Harlem Health Center, a famous cooperative project of twenty-one agencies; reorganization of the nursing committee into an executive committee, committee of the whole, and local committees; opening of the new administration building at 99 Park Avenue, the urgent need for which was first presented to the nursing committee by Miss Goodrich in July, 1917; the inception at Teachers College, through the efforts of Miss Nutting, of a combined theoretical and field course covering a period from eighteen months to two years, leading to a certificate of the college and credited toward the B.S. degree and professional diploma.

In addition to professional activities, Miss Goodrich took a personal interest in the nurses. During January, 1922, the staff "had great pleasure and fun in dining in sections with Miss Goodrich at the Cosmopolitan Club," according to nursing committee notes. About thirty nurses were entertained at a time and there were outside speakers. The facilities of the Cosmopolitan Club were made available, Miss Goodrich says, through the generosity of Mary Magoun Brown, one of many personal contributions

69

which Miss Brown made to the enjoyment and well-being of the staff.

~~~~~~

A program for the public extending over several days, referred to as Dedication Week, marked the opening on January 10, 1923, of the central administration building at 99 Park Avenue, given to the Visiting Nurse Service of the Henry Street Settlement as a memorial to Mr. Jacob H. Schiff. Mr. Paul Cravath, who presided, remarked that "We are commemorating the triumph of a great idea." Governor and Mrs. Smith came down from Albany to take part in the program. Two of the speakers of whom we shall wish to take note were Annie W. Goodrich and Professor C.-E. A. Winslow, whose eyes were already gazing upon distant horizons for nursing.

Miss Goodrich called her address "The Tale of a Third City" and into it she has put the spirit of the impelling future which shines through the activities of her career. Letting her speak for herself, we hear her say:

"The request to interpret the relation of this beautiful building to the Visiting Nurse Service administered by Henry Street Settlement accords indeed a great privilege and honor but it imposes also a truly great responsibility.

"Were I to give a title for my thoughts, it would be—'The Tale of a Third City'—for like 'The Tale of Two Cities' by Charles Dickens, we are concerned tonight in a momentous period of the world's history, with a house on the corner, the story of a young woman and devoted friends, and the echo of many feet. Do you recall, I wonder, that chapter in which on a stormy night in the house on the corner, the little group meets, around whom Dickens was to weave his story of the French Revolution?

" 'There was a great hurry in the streets. The wonderful corner for echoes resounded with the echoes of footsteps coming and going, yet not a footstep was there . . . I have sometimes made the echoes out to be the echoes of all the footsteps that are coming by and by into our lives.'

" 'Dickens had,' said Chesterton, 'if ever man had, the key of the street. His earth was the stones of the street; his stars were the lamps of the street; his hero was the man in the street. He could open the inmost door of his house—the door that leads into that secret passage which is lined with houses and roofed with stars.' "

The momentous period in history of which Miss Goodrich speaks was a time of reconstruction after a devastating war. The hope for peace, a great and healthy peace, was in the air. The footsteps which she heard were those, no doubt, of all who would seek to build a world fit for the needs and the aspirations of humanity.

When Miss Wald likened Miss Goodrich to a spirit afire, was it something of this thought and this conviction which she saw?

A few months hence, in June, 1923, the announcement was to be made that Miss Goodrich had been appointed dean of the new school of nursing at

Yale. For a year there had been a great "hurry in the streets" and much questioning as to where the new school was to be located—ever since Dr. C.-E. A. Winslow's condensation of the now famous Rockefeller-Goldmark report on "Nursing and Nursing Education in the United States" was presented to the 5,000 nurses attending the Biennial Convention of the national nursing organizations in Seattle in June of 1922.

～～～～

Cars marked "Nurses, let's go!" could have been signaled in any part of the city to take you wherever directed, if you had been one of the delegates to the Biennial. Seattle was decked with garden roses for the occasion. Headquarters at the Y.W.C.A. resounded with gay feminine greetings and earnest talk. From the far corners of the United States and Canada these women had gathered to consider once again their mutual problems and the destiny of American nursing.

On Monday evening, June 26th, the delegates met in joint session to hear Miss Goodrich address them on "The Objective of the Nurse in a Democracy," printed in the *American Journal of Nursing* for September, 1922. Wednesday afternoon, again in joint session, Carolyn E. Gray spoke on "Ideals of the Nursing Profession for Schools for Nurses"; Clara D. Noyes on "Relation of Nursing Education to Community and National Welfare"; and Dr. Richard Olding Beard of the University of Minnesota on "Modern Education of Women for the Profession of Nursing." And Wednesday evening, June 28th, Miss Goodrich read to the delegates the abstract prepared by Professor Winslow of Yale, "A Recent Study of the Education of the Nurse—Report of the Committee for Study of Nursing Education of the Rockefeller Foundation."

Reactions to this historic report were summed up by Ethel Johns of the University of British Columbia on Friday morning: "We are not quite sure whether our elaborate structure of education has crashed about our ears, or whether, as we vaguely hope, though the foundations are shaken, it still stands four square to all the winds of controversy which sweep about it."

Ethel Johns told a story which speaks for all who might have felt they were attacked by the Rockefeller report:

I remember very clearly one small hospital. It served a small northern community then in the early stages of development. Its board of directors was composed of farmers of the district; its ambulance was the patrol of the Royal Northwest Mounted Police; its "matron" a youngster of 22 just out of training; its nursing staff a group of three pupils who had never seen the inside of a high school. . . . Better nursing had been done, no doubt, but none more devoted than those three pupils afforded their patients under conditions of almost hopeless discouragement.

From an educational point of view their training school, as they fondly called it—poor children—was a pitiful joke. But the community it served did not

73

see it quite that way. They were absurdly grateful. You see, some of them would have died if the hospital had not been there.

Perhaps we had better remember these human values when we are obliged to standardize these schools out of existence, because of course they will have to go very soon. But should not the Rockefeller Report's ringing challenge speak less loudly than the cry of human need? These schools must not be destroyed until something better has been established to take their place. Let us remember that.

The winds of controversy stirred up by the Rockefeller report are still blowing today, having been given new vigor with the publication of *Nursing for the Future*, by Esther Lucile Brown, in 1948. The burden of the challenge, then as now, is the sweeping criticism of many of the existing schools of nursing—whose first responsibility it is to supply the hospitals with willing hands and feet, and only secondarily to give the student nurse the variety of experience and the background of scientific and social information which she will need as a graduate nurse if her service to humanity is to be truly professional in character. The schools of nursing, particularly the smaller ones, felt themselves under attack.

No one has expressed the conflict which this arouses in the nurse more clearly than Ethel Johns, to whom the first course for nurses at Teachers College in 1899 meant that "we had touched the hem of the garment." For nurses would not be nurses if their first aim were not to prevent useless waste of human life and relieve the suffering which is experienced in times of accident or illness. Yet they realize—as the general public often does not—what tragedy can result from placing responsibility in hands that lack the intelligent skill which results from mastery of both the science and the art of nursing.

The "distinct and definite value" of the small school to the community was championed by Miss Goodrich during a discussion period at the 1914 Convention of the National League of Nursing Education. She suggested then that these smaller schools be brought into a more favorable position in one of two ways; namely, by affiliation with large schools, or by carrying a two-year course and then sending their students to larger hospitals for a period before the diploma of nursing is granted, being given credit for one year in a school having a three-year course. A few years later, the idea of central schools of nursing was being presented as the best way of meeting the broader needs for integration of rural and urban health services. The development of central schools requires drastic changes in organization and is today still in its infancy. One of the outstanding models is to be found at Western Reserve University, where, however, the geographical distribution of cooperating hospitals is entirely urban.

The medical profession, by and large, and hospital administrators, as well as lay people, have been slow to recognize the merits and the potentialities of the nurse's claim to a need for truly professional education. Large groups, as well as hotheaded individuals, have taken sides in the controversy. Conservative elements have hesitated even to experiment with a

75

new approach to the problem. Therefore it is the greater wonder that Yale University should have accepted the school of nursing which was set up to test the recommendations of the Rockefeller report.

~~~~~

The work which went into this historic report began just a few weeks after the armistice, in December, 1918, when the Rockefeller Foundation called a conference of about fifty persons interested in the development of public health nursing in the United States. The introduction to the published report states: "The primary object of the meeting was a discussion of the status of public health nursing in the United States and of the education desirable for training the needed personnel. On these two points all shades of opinion were expressed by those present; there was substantial agreement, however, that the usual three years' hospital training was not, in and by itself, satisfactory for preparing public health nurses."

The conference requested that a committee be appointed to study the questions raised and to "prepare a definite proposal for a course of training for public health nurses." This committee soon found that the whole subject of nursing education would have to be considered. The result is the 585-page report prepared by Josephine Goldmark entitled "Nursing and Nursing Education in the United States," which was finally published in 1923.

Working with Miss Goldmark in the preparation of this report was a committee on which are to be found, among others, names previously mentioned as comprising the Committee on Nursing of the Council of National Defense in 1917. With Dr. C.-E. A. Winslow as chairman, the original committee of seven included the following: Mary Beard, Boston; Dr. H. M. Biggs, New York; Annie W. Goodrich, New York; M. Adelaide Nutting, New York; Lillian D. Wald, New York; and Dr. William H. Welch, Baltimore.

Mary Beard, director of the Instructive District Nursing Association of Boston and president of the National Organization for Public Health Nursing, was later to become associate director of the International Health Division of the Rockefeller Foundation. It was her responsibility to recommend, or not to recommend, the Foundation's million-dollar endowment of the Yale University School of Nursing when, by 1928, it had proved itself through the initial five years of trial and experimentation.

Miss Beard began her career as a visiting nurse on her graduation from the New York Hospital School of Nursing in 1904. Speaking before the Institute for Board Members under the auspices of the Henry Street Visiting Nurse Service in New York in 1930, Miss Goodrich told this story—which she identifies now as relating to Miss Beard:

Approximately a quarter of a century ago a clergyman came to the office of the school of nursing of which I was then superintendent seeking a nurse capable of developing a visiting nursing organization in his town, presenting the required qualifications as follows:

"You are, I believe, from New England. You will

therefore I am sure understand the type of committee interested in forwarding such a project—cultured, refined, conservative, intellectual persons. It would be important for this young woman to be a socially acceptable guest, one who could attend their dinners, contribute to the conversation and secure their interest, for upon her personality would greatly depend the raising of the required funds for the undertaking."

The hospital facilities of the town were not great and the dispensary facilities almost lacking. It would seem advisable therefore for her to be familiar with minor surgical conditions so that she could treat, before leaving in the morning, any cases that might come in to her. Drugs, as one knows, are expensive. A well-trained graduate would be supposed to have sufficient knowledge to perhaps put up the less important prescriptions and prepare ointments, solutions, etc. . . . She should be the type of woman who was not afraid to render any needed service, but finding the mother ill would give the needed care, roll up her sleeves, bathe the baby, wash the dishes, scrub the floor—the hungry, tired husband returning to find his house in order, his sick wife looked after, the children fed and clean, the dinner awaiting him. . . . Ah, yes, salary. The salary would indeed be moderate, but, his face brightening, he was sure to the type of woman he was describing the salary would be of small importance.

The required personality was found. Somewhat over a year later he sought a successor with the encouraging statement that the appointee had measured up in every particular he thought but one. She did not seem to have sufficient endurance. She had broken down—yes, quite completely broken down —and he would like someone like her to fill her place.

Fortunately Mary Beard recovered from this initiation to join in the cause of strengthening the nurse's education and defining her field of service.

The Committee for the Study of Nursing Education, financed by the Rockefeller Foundation, was enlarged as the study went along to include Dr. Livingston Farrand of Washington, Dr. L. Emmett Holt of New York, Miss Julia C. Lathrop of Washington, Mrs. John Lowman of Cleveland, Dr. David L. Edsall of Boston, Dr. E. G. Stillman of New York, Miss Lillian S. Clayton of Philadelphia, Dr. Lewis A. Conner of New York, Dr. C. G. Parnall of Ann Arbor, Dr. Thomas W. Salmon of New York, Dr. Winford H. Smith of Baltimore, and Miss Helen Wood of St. Louis.

During the second year of the study, Miss Goldmark was assisted by Carolyn E. Gray, formerly superintendent of nurses at City Hospital, New York, who went on to Western Reserve University to head the Department of Nursing Education there during the period of planning for the university school of nursing which opened in Cleveland in 1923 and was made possible by the endowment contributed by Mrs. Frances Payne Bolton. Laura M. Grant, director of nursing services at the New Haven Unit of the Grace–New Haven Community Hospital, who was in Cleveland at the time, remembers well the visits which Miss Goodrich paid to them during the early years and their reliance on her experienced counsel.

What the Committee for the Study of Nursing Education established was the fact that the apprenticeship system of training nurses was a "slow and cumbrous method of education; that it often has not even the virtues of a true apprenticeship wherein pupils work directly under the eye of a master." As a result of the study, the committee drew up a list of ten conclusions, or recommendations, to serve as a guide to the future development of nursing as a profession based on sound educational policies.

The core—no, the very heart—of these recommendations was to be found in the tenth and final "Conclusion," namely, that "The development of nursing service adequate for the care of the sick and for the conduct of the modern public health campaign demands as an absolute prerequisite the securing of funds for the endowment of nursing education of all types; and that it is of primary importance to provide reasonably generous endowment for university schools of nursing."

It was also recommended that for public health nursing a postgraduate course in addition to the basic hospital training be required; that young women of "high capacity" be attracted to the career of nursing; that attempts to lower standards be resisted by legislation; that a subsidiary grade of nursing service, with training courses of eight or nine months, be established and licensed; that "the average hospital training school is not organized on such a basis as to conform to the standards accepted in other educational fields; that it would be possible to reduce the period of hospital training to twenty-eight months by eliminating unessential, non-educational routine"; that superintendents, supervisors, instructors, and public health nurses should in all cases receive special additional training beyond the basic nursing course; and that "the development and strengthening of University Schools of Nursing is of fundamental importance in the furtherance of nursing education."

Miss Nutting was able to concur with the recommendation that the period of hospital training could be reduced. She was of course jubilant that the need for endowment of nursing education was at last to be widely recognized, and the emphasis on developing university schools of nursing met with her hearty approval. With these conclusions, Miss Nutting and Miss Goodrich had no quarrel.

They were, however—as has been mentioned earlier—extremely sensitive on the matter of the aide or subsidiary nurse. Dr. Winslow, as chairman of the committee, knew that neither of them would agree to the recommendations for the development of subsidiary nurses unless a miracle happened. Other members of the committee were so firmly convinced as to the necessity for inclusion of these recommendations that it would be equally impossible to get the final report unanimously endorsed without them, and Dr. Winslow felt that unanimity was needed to have the "Conclusions" carry weight in years to come.

The strategy of a diplomat was obviously going to be required. Before he called the committee together for the final session at which each member would be asked to sign the report, Dr. Winslow arranged for a couple of preliminary meetings at which the varying shades of opinion in this group of experts might be expressed. And then—the miracle happened. Miss Nutting and Miss Goodrich, and one or two others who held minor reservations, agreed to sign their names to the "Conclusions" in order that the entire report should not be held from publication.

"I recall with particular vividness the preparation of this Committee Report," said Dr. Winslow, speaking at the twenty-fifth anniversary exercises of the Yale School of Nursing in New Haven in 1949. "It was completed at an evening meeting when Miss Goodrich and I and others sat around a table in the garden behind the Henry Street Settlement, working by candle light"—a significant place for the signing of a document which had its inception in the interest of a great foundation in the field of public health.

Miss Goodrich, who believed in the expression of minority opinions, gave her minority report at the annual meeting of the New York State Nurses' Association in October, 1922. She had signed with the other members of the committee, but she wished to add that it was her opinion that admission standards in all schools of nursing should permit the carrying of work of university grade, adding that she could not "subscribe to a shortening of the period of training to less than three years for those who have not had two or more years of college work."

Her thinking had changed somewhat regarding the training of attendants since her 1911 recommendations to the State Education Department in New York. "My belief in the need of such a subsidiary group is not less strong today than it was then," she said in 1922. "My method of meeting this need has in more than one aspect distinctly changed. . . . Today we see that for those workers who are to deal effectively with the convalescent period of sickness is required an extensive body of knowledge in which psychology, psychiatry, the therapies, etc., play an important part. For those to whom we would relegate the simpler nursing tasks, we would emphasize the importance of the provision of instruction that will insure tactile skill and technical efficiency for each task, no matter how simple, but we also believe that the hours of duty should be such as to make it possible for these young women, if young they are, to make up their deficiencies in secondary work, while filling these positions, in order that they may enter the nursing profession."

Miss Goodrich pointed out that not only was the emphatic statement of the importance of endowments for schools of nursing to be concurred in, but that "a not less important step to be taken is the provision of 'A Sounder Economic Basis for Every Hospital,'" adding that "Health has become the business of the people. No business is carried on effectively, or indeed at all, that does not provide for the payment of labor. Our communities today must no longer lay the burden of the care of the sick on the workers for the sake of their own health, not less than for the sake of the workers themselves."

That the Rockefeller Foundation had been searching for a university in which to set up a new school
of nursing on a truly educational basis was the hope-
ful assumption of the nurses who listened to Dr.
Winslow's condensation of the Goldmark report
when it was read by Miss Goodrich in Seattle. Cleveland was known to be working on such a plan, in
which Mrs. Bolton was interested not only as a financial contributor but also as a moving spirit. And as
long ago as 1915, Miss Nutting in her capacity as
director of the Department of Nursing and Health
at Teachers College had reported to the National
League of Nursing Education:

There are some important problems before the
Department relating to its future and the way in
which its growth shall be directed. . . . The next
logical step forward is the development of a University Training School for Nurses in connection, of
course, with some hospital of proper standing. To
establish such a school on such a basis as would insure
sound educational work would mean an endowment
of about one million dollars. . . . It is . . . a practical plan for placing at least one School of Nursing
on a sound economic basis. I look forward confi-
dently to the upbuilding of such a school in connection with this University.

Miss Nutting's dream—shared by Miss Maxwell,
superintendent of nurses at Presbyterian—came a
step nearer its realization in 1917, when a relationship was established with the school of nursing of
the Presbyterian Hospital which made it possible to
offer a combination of courses leading to a B.S. degree at the university and to the diploma of nursing.

The death of Mr. William Sloane, president of the Board of Managers of the Presbyterian Hospital, struck a severe blow in 1922 to the hopes for the endowment which he was interested in securing for the school of nursing. Though their personal disappointment was deep, both Miss Maxwell and Miss Nutting were none the less eager that an endowed school should come into being somewhere. Such hopes as these were widespread in nursing circles.

The University of Michigan, through the interest of Dr. Christopher G. Parnall, director of the University Hospital in Ann Arbor and a member of the Rockefeller committee, took up the consideration of an independent university school of nursing in 1922, but the plan failed to be passed by the regents of the university.

Dr. David L. Edsall, dean of the Harvard Medical School, and Dr. Livingston Farrand, president of Cornell University, were interested in such a plan, but satisfactory arrangements could not be brought to completion in either of these institutions. At Johns Hopkins, a conservative tradition was opposed to a change in administrative setup, and at the same time the Rockefeller Foundation was already contributing to the financing of the School of Hygiene and Public Health.

The great problem was that while some persons in almost every university could be found who were interested in the plan, powerful and conservative elements were opposed. To place the education of nurses on a par with that of physicians, lawyers, architects, teachers, and other groups being prepared by American universities was considered a most radical suggestion.

Even within the Rockefeller Foundation, some of the officers and trustees were skeptical. At any rate it was found expedient to propose the backing of a five-year experiment rather than an outright endowment, which would be forthcoming at the end of five years, should the school of nursing prove successful.

To Edwin R. Embree, then secretary of the Rockefeller Foundation and for some years president of the Rosenwald Fund, goes much of the credit for working out a way by which the officers could be brought to some basis of accord. It was through Mr. Embree and with him that the final details of the grant to the school of nursing at Yale were worked out. He recalls how the backers of the school and of other unconventional projects in the foundation spoke of themselves as the "young Turks," so revolutionary did such plans seem at the time.

One of the older, established universities in the East was obviously going to have to be chosen. Vanderbilt University, in which the foundation was interested, was considered too young an institution for radical ventures and its scope as a segregated university too limited for a national demonstration.

~~~~~

Yale University and the city of New Haven, on the other hand, offered ground which was ripe for experimentation. The Yale Medical School was in the process of receiving transfusions, both educationally and financially, under Dean George Blumer and his successor, Dr. Milton C. Winternitz, both of whom regarded the education of nurses as a factor directly related to the usefulness of the clinical field in the education of physicians. President James Rowland Angell of Yale had been an officer of the Carnegie Corporation and was one in spirit with the "young Turks" to whom Mr. Embree refers. His background in coeducation had given him a sure faith in women and their role.

Most significant was the fact that the chairman of the Rockefeller-Goldmark Committee, Dr. C.-E. A. Winslow, was then professor of public health at Yale, whence he had come in 1915 from the New York State Department of Health, the College of the City of New York, and Teachers College, Columbia University. Since 1910, the year which he places as marking the beginning of the campaign for education in personal hygiene as a major public health objective, he had been lecturing once a week to the nurses at Teachers College, continuing even after he moved to New Haven. His participation as a member of the faculty of the Vassar camp and his activities on many committees concerned with nursing in the United States and abroad during the period of the war and its aftermath attest to the depth of his belief in the nurse as the "essential field agent in public health work" and his insistence that her education is a vital necessity.

Miss Wald, in recognition of his contributions, said of Dr. Winslow in 1922: "He has humanized the university," to which he brought "the conception of the dignity of human service." Certainly he had given unstintingly of his time and counsel that the nurse might become not merely a practitioner but also a teacher.

The Connecticut Training School for Nurses at the New Haven Hospital was to celebrate its fiftieth birthday on June 12, 1923. The charter of this school, granted by the Connecticut legislature in 1873, provided for the separate organization of a training school for nurses. The directors of the General Hospital Society of Connecticut were to afford to the school such facilities for instruction as could be granted at the hospital. In the yearly report of the school for 1881 are to be found these impatient words:

It is perhaps well to state once for all, the school is thankful they are able to relieve suffering in the Hospital, but the school does not exist primarily for this purpose, but for the training of nurses for the public; the only school in this country or in Europe which is not supported by the Hospital which it serves.

Mrs. Frances Bacon, wife of a distinguished New Haven physician, was the guiding spirit of the board of directors of this school to the end of her life, and for thirty-three years it was possible to direct and finance the school without assistance from the hospital.

A "Resumé of the History of the Connecticut Training School for Nurses" by Margaret Stack in the *American Journal of Nursing* for July, 1923, notes that "the first visiting nursing done in this city and probably in the state was started by the Training

88

School in 1888 when it furnished, free of charge, a nurse for the sick poor of New Haven," a service which had to be withdrawn two years later due to lack of funds. The school began sending its students for a six weeks' affiliation with the New Haven Visiting Nurse Association in 1906.

Thus the plan for an independent school had its precedent, and the interest in public health nursing was also one of long standing.

The New Haven Visiting Nurse Association, under the directorship of Mary Grace Hills, was far advanced in an educational direction. For some years an eight-months course in public health for graduate nurses had been given in cooperation with Yale University. Miss Hills wrote Miss Goodrich in June, 1923, that "we have only been waiting for the establishment of a university school of nursing at Yale to turn the course over to the proper authorities." The board of directors, on which Mrs. C.-E. A. Winslow served as a member of the educational committee, were interested in cooperating with the plan, which represented "the realization of a dream of many years."

The New Haven Hospital, with a bed capacity of around four hundred, offered clinical experience in medicine, surgery, pediatrics, obstetrics, communicable disease, and its outpatient department was a promising field to be developed for teaching. The School of Medicine was prepared to allow members of its faculty to participate in offering classes for nurses, and Dr. Willard C. Rappleye, superintendent of the New Haven Hospital, held a broad conception of the hospital's function in the health movement.

Miss Goodrich, before the announcement of her appointment as dean, was asked to make a survey of the New Haven Hospital and other facilities which would offer potential clinical fields for a school of nursing. She returned from New Haven enthusiastic over the remarkable readiness of the community to participate in such an experiment as was under consideration. The plan which she outlined for the school represented the fruition of her thirty years in nursing, her association with the main currents of educational progress, and her seasoned special interest in democratic administration.

~~~~~~

The lead article in the *American Journal of Nursing* for June, 1923, is entitled "Dawn of a New Era in Nursing Education." The two new university schools of nursing, one at Yale and the other at Western Reserve—for the first time assured of autonomy within the framework of institutions of higher learning in America—were hailed, figuratively if not literally, with a burst of applause. Here we read:

The most significant feature of the Yale School is the character of the training itself. An attempt will be made to present all the factors which contribute toward the diagnosis, care and treatment of disease and which have relationship to the conservation of health. Patients will not be considered as hospital "cases" only, but such factors as heredity, environment, child development, psychology, economics, sociology, industry, and public health will be presented in their bearing upon each problem as it is studied. Such a plan will emphasize sickness in its true relationship as a family, community, and public health problem and to properly develop such a conception, the new school will embrace field work and community nursing as a part of the basic training.

The same issue of the *Journal* reports the stirring celebration of Bellevue's Semi-Centennial in Carnegie Hall on May 8, 1923, the auditorium completely filled with nurses. Miss Goodrich's address, "The Soul of America," began and ended with this quotation from *The Science of Power* by Benjamin Kidd:

When the mind of the West comes to grasp in all its far-reaching application the fact that the science of power in the social integration is the science of directing the collective will over long stretches of time to definite ends through the emotion of the ideal, it will be the first step to a new order of civilization.

Old Eli had accepted as one of his own the poet and the prophet of nursing. The Rockefeller Foundation had given her "the key to the street." The progress and policies of the new school were to be developed in the climate of Yale, free from control by the foundation. Annie W. Goodrich, bringing with her the highest aspirations of nurses and friends of the healing arts, was to dedicate herself anew—as she dedicated her book, *The Social and Ethical Significance of Nursing*, in 1932—"To my students."

Her concept of community service a practical goal, her definition of nursing a creative challenge, it was of less import to her that she should have become the first dean of an independent school of nursing having its own governing board, its own faculties, its own classrooms, and its own budget, than that nursing should gain some day full opportunity to contribute to the building of a healthy citizenry. The "key to the street" which had been given to her by a great foundation would—she trusted—one day be placed in the hands of every nurse in the new era ushered in by the generations waging the ideological battles of the present century.

Yet the apparent munificence of the million-dollar endowment which assured the permanence of the school of nursing at Yale in 1928 is indicative of the status of nursing education even after all the progress of the intervening years. This is still an age when, as Dr. Winslow pointed out at the twenty-fifth anniversary exercises of the Yale school in 1949, "It is fair to assume that in the overwhelming majority of hospital schools, the student gets only what she pays for in tuition and service—and often receives even less than she contributes. The lack of budgeting and accounting methods makes any close estimate of financing resources impossible. Many hospital schools, including some of the most outstanding schools in large metropolitan centers, have no budget of their own at all. It is probable, however, that the total amount of endowment income, foundation grants, and support available for schools of nursing cannot be in excess of four million dollars annually and is probably not over two million. The medical schools for this country have for 1948–49 a combined total budget of 51 million dollars, of which only one-fourth will come from tuition, 40 per cent from endowments, gifts, and general university funds, and 35 per cent from state and municipal taxes.

"Even in Connecticut with one of the very few endowed schools of nursing in the country, nursing education receives less than one-eighth as much as medical education and about one-fourth as much as teacher training, and I doubt very much if any other state could show ratios even as high as these."

~~~~~

Her critics have called Miss Goodrich "ambitious" and "difficult to understand." Ever a formidable opponent, an astute knowledge of when and when not to compromise would be revealed in an analysis of her administrative actions. Men who have worked with her would probably agree with Dr. Franklin H. Martin's characterization of her, during the days of the campaign for the Army school, as a female "Old Hickory" who could "argue Will Mayo to a standstill," granting her the masculine respect and admiration which does much to explain her acceptance in a world hitherto reserved for themselves.

If it can be grasped that the leadership of a great objective can embolden even a sensitive woman in a slender frame to stand at any cost for the principles to which that end is irrevocably linked, perhaps an explanation can be found for the consistency with which this daughter of New England has found the stamina and the courage throughout her entire career to face up to almost overwhelming odds in order that she might "guide and guard the stumbling, halting steps of our civilization on its long pilgrimage toward the ideal."

93

REFERENCES

Alumnae News, Yale University School of Nursing, Yale University Press, New Haven, 1946.

American Journal of Nursing, especially the issues for December, 1922; May, 1923; June, 1923; June, 1925; and July, 1934.

Brown, Esther Lucile, *Nursing for the Future*, Russell Sage Foundation, New York, 1948.

Chase, John W., ed., *Years of the Modern—An American Appraisal*, Longmans, Green and Co., New York and Toronto, 1949.

Dock, Lavinia L., and others, *History of American Red Cross Nursing*, The Macmillan Company, New York, 1922.

Dufton, Lena, *History of Nursing at the New York Post-Graduate Medical School and Hospital*, The Alumnae Association, New York, 1944.

Flexner, Abraham, "Medical Education in the United States and Canada," Carnegie Foundation, Bulletin No. 4, New York, 1910.

Goldmark, Josephine, *Nursing and Nursing Education in the United States*, The Macmillan Company, New York, 1923.

Goodrich, Annie W., "The Nursing Program of the Army," *Modern Hospital*, November, 1918.

——, "The Objective of the Nurse in a Democracy," *American Journal of Nursing*, September, 1922.

——, *The Social and Ethical Significance of Nursing*, The Macmillan Company, New York, 1932.

——, "The University, the School of Nursing, and the Subsidiary Group," *American Journal of Nursing*, May, 1923.

Henry Street Nurse, The. Issues from December, 1920, through 1923. (Miss Montanye, March, 1921; Dedication Week, January–February, 1922; Dinner for Miss Maxwell, February–March, 1922; Army School, April–May, 1922; Biennial in Seattle, August–September, 1922; Miss Goodrich, May–June, 1923.)

Hughes, Dorothea M., "History of the Army School of Nursing," *Annual of the Army School*, pp. 30–34, 1921.

Johns, Ethel, "Administration in Schools of Nursing," *Proceedings, National League of Nursing Education*, pp. 255–59, 1922.

———, "The Nurse Seeks the University," *The Canadian Nurse*, September, 1948.

Kidd, Benjamin, *The Science of Power*, G. P. Putnam's Sons, New York, 1918.

Lee, Eleanor, *History of the School of Nursing of the Presbyterian Hospital, New York, 1892–1942*, G. P. Putnam's Sons, New York, 1942.

Martin, Franklin H., *The Joy of Living—an Autobiography*, vol. II, p. 359, Doubleday, Doran & Co., New York, 1936.

Munson, Helen, *The Story of the National League of Nursing Education*, W. B. Saunders Co., Philadelphia and London, 1942.

Noyes, Clara D., "M. Adelaide Nutting: Some Reminiscences," *The Red Cross Courier*, June 15, 1925.

Nutting, M. Adelaide, *A Sound Economic Basis for Schools of Nursing*, G. P. Putnam's Sons, New York and London, 1926.

Proceedings, American Society of Superintendents of Training Schools for Nurses, and *Annual Reports*, National League of Nursing Education, 1897–1923.

Stack, Margaret, "Resumé of the History of the Connecticut Training School for Nurses," *American Journal of Nursing*, July, 1923.

95

Stewart, Isabel M., "M. Adelaide Nutting: Appreciations," *American Journal of Nursing*, June, 1925.

Thermometer, The. Publication of the Vassar Training Camp, issues for June 27, 1918; January, 1919; and November, 1919.

Van Blarcom, Carolyn C., "Miss Nutting Resigns," *Modern Hospital*, June, 1925.

Wald, Lillian D., "Comrade Annie W. G.," *The Henry Street Nurse*, May–June, 1923.

Williams, Beryl, *Lillian Wald: Angel of Henry Street*, Julian Messner, Inc., New York, 1948.

Winslow, C.-E. A., "Dreams and Awakenings, 25th Anniversary Exercises of the Yale University School of Nursing," *Yale Journal of Biology and Medicine*, March, 1949.

———, "The Evolution of Public Health and its Objectives," in *Public Health in the World Today*, ed. by James S. Simmons, Harvard University Press, Cambridge, 1949.

———, "The Role of the Visiting Nurse in the Campaign for Public Health," *American Journal of Nursing*, August, 1911.

Yost, Edna, *American Women of Nursing*, J. B. Lippincott Co., Philadelphia and New York, 1947.

INDEX

INDEX

Gray, Carolyn E., 62, 72, 79
Greenwich House, 69

Hadley, Mrs. Morris, 51
Hana, M., 64
Harmer, Bertha, 54
Harvard Medical School, 85
Henry Street Nurse, The, 9, 42, 43, 44, 64, 66, 68
Henry Street Settlement, 10, 14, 44, 64, 82
Henry Street Settlement, Visiting Nurse Service, 5,
   34, 42, 44, 46, 59, 63, 64, 67, 68, 69, 70, 77
Hills, Mary Grace, 89
Hodgman, Gertrude, 66
Hodgson, Jane, 18
Holt, L. Emmett, 79
Hudson, Lillian A., 46

Instructive Visiting Nurse Service, Boston, 77
International Council of Nurses, 32, 35
Ireland, General, 60

Jenkins, Mrs. Helen Hartley, 22
Johns, Ethel, 73, 74
Johns Hopkins Hospital, 22
Johns Hopkins University, 85
Johnson, Florence M., 68
Johnson, Helen, 54

Lathrop, Julia, 49, 51, 79
Letterman General Hospital, 60
Loeb, Traper Company, 67, 68
Lowman, Mrs. John, 79
Ludlam, George P., 8

McNutt, Julia C., 12, 15
Manhattan Eye and Ear Hospital, 14
Martin, Franklin H., 93
Massachusetts General Hospital, 54
Maxwell, Anna C., 9, 14, 18, 22, 26, 48, 84, 85
Mayo, William, 93
Mayor's Council on National Defense, New York City,
   33, 50

Rappleye, Willard C., 89
Reeve, Irma, 65
Registration of nurses, 28–29, 53
Robb, Isabel Hampton, 21
Robson, Emilie G., 65
Rockefeller Foundation, 51, 54, 72, 73, 76, 77, 80, 82, 84, 85, 86, 87, 91, 92
Roosa, Daniel B. St. John, 13, 14
Roosevelt Hospital, New York City, 14

Sabin, Florence, 54
St. Elizabeth's Hospital, New York City, 14
St. Luke's Hospital, New York City, 20–21, 54
St. Mark's Hospital, New York City, 14
Salmon, Thomas W., 79
Samuel, Mary, 14, 17
Sanburn, Katherine, 17
San Francisco Visiting Nurse Association, 41
Schiff, Jacob F., 70
Shatz, Rebecca, 65
Sloane, William, 85
Sloane Hospital, New York City, 11, 12, 16
Smith, Alfred E., 70
Smith, Winford H., 50, 57, 58, 59, 79
Social Service Exchange, 68
Spanish-American War, 17, 48
Staten Island Civic League, 45–46
Stewart, Isabel M., 39, 45, 52
Stillman, E. G., 79
Stimson, Julia C., 23 ff., 49, 53, 61, 62
Strong, Anne, 52
Sutliffe, Irene, 10, 17, 18

Taylor, Effie J., 21, 35
Teachers College, Columbia University, 4, 20, 22, 26, 30, 32, 33, 45, 49, 50, 59, 64, 69, 74, 84, 87
Thermometer, The, 55, 56
Thompson, Dora, 57

Vanderbilt University, 86
Van Zandt, Mrs. Ada, 15
Vassar Training Camp, 51, 52–55, 61, 87

Wald, Lillian D., 10, 14, 31, 34, 35, 36, 37, 38, 40, 41, 44, 45, 47, 49, 50, 52, 63, 71, 77, 87
Walter Reed Hospital, 60
Warburg, Mrs. Paul W., 45, 65, 68
Washington University, St. Louis, 53
Welch, William H., 50, 77
Western Reserve University School of Nursing, 62, 75, 79, 90
Williams, A. W., 54
Winslow, C.-E. A., 30, 50, 54, 56, 64, 70, 72, 73, 77, 81, 84, 87, 92
Winslow, Mrs. C.-E. A., 89
Winternitz, Milton C., 87
Wolf, Anna D., 54
Women's Clubs, Federation of, 59
Wood, Helen, 79

Yale University, 6, 51, 76, 86
Yale University School of Medicine, 86, 89
Yale University School of Nursing, 2, 3, 4, 6, 21, 71, 77, 82, 86, 90, 92